新东方SAT/ACT课程指定用书

美国高考
核心3000词

练习册

新东方SAT/ACT考试研究院 ▪

熊正煜 姚莹 徐静 主编 ▪

浙江教育出版社·杭州

图书在版编目(CIP)数据

美国高考核心3000词 / 熊正煜，姚莹，徐静主编
．—杭州：浙江教育出版社，2017.4
ISBN 978-7-5536-5396-9

Ⅰ.①美… Ⅱ.①熊… ②姚… ③徐… Ⅲ.①英语—
词汇—高等学校—入学考试—美国—自学参考资料 Ⅳ.
①H313

中国版本图书馆CIP数据核字（2017）第033800号

美国高考核心3000词
MEIGUO GAOKAO HEXIN 3000CI

主　　编	熊正煜　姚　莹　徐　静
责任编辑	孔令宇
美术编辑	韩　波
封面设计	李　倩
责任校对	刘文芳
责任印务	时小娟

出版发行	浙江教育出版社
	（杭州市天目山路40号　　邮编：310013）
印　　刷	北京鑫丰华彩印有限公司
开　　本	787mm×1092mm　1/16
成品尺寸	185mm×260mm
印　　张	30
字　　数	722 000
版　　次	2017年4月第1版
印　　次	2017年4月第1次印刷
标准书号	ISBN 978-7-5536-5396-9
定　　价	68.00元
联系电话	0571 - 85170300 - 80928
电子邮箱	dywh@xdf.cn
网　　址	www.zjeph.com

目录
CONTENTS

1 仅仅完成单词认知往往不能转化为分数的提升；因此强烈建议考生重视这份结合语境与单词运用的配套练习。

2 预热级练习与预热级词表同步完成，建议每完成一个 List 的记忆之后就完成相应练习。

3 每份练习包含 10 组"7 选 5 句子填空"。考生可以先将 7 个单词的中文意思填在单词下方的方框里，再根据上下文，在句子的空格处填入最恰当的单词。

4 所有练习皆配有答案。

Word List 1

Group 1

constant	approach	crucial	principal
exclude	suspect	lean	

1. It was perfectly all right, he said, because the police had not _____ him of anything.
2. The average speed of the winds remained _____.
3. Improved consumer confidence is _____ to an economic recovery.
4. As autumn _____, the plants and colors in the garden changed.
5. Their _____ concern is bound to be that of winning the next general election.

Group 2

justify	alternative	phase	convention
swing	substantial	yield	

1. The social services account for a _____ part of public spending.
2. He sets at naught every _____ of society.
3. Last year 400,000 acres of land _____ a crop worth $ 1.75 billion.
4. No argument can _____ a war.
5. _____ treatments can provide a useful back-up to conventional treatment.

Group 3

perceive	consistent	attach	incorporate
underlie	commission	innovation	

1. New goals are not always _____ with the existing policies.
2. The Contractor shall _____ all the study findings and recommendations.
3. Voters _____ him as a decisive and resolute international leader.
4. We must promote originality and encourage _____.
5. Psychological problems often _____ apparently physical disorders.

Group 4

depression	internal	assume	core
variation	distinguish	perspective	

1. Unlike the temporary workers, our _____ team is in place to perform the main tasks.
2. It is necessary to _____ the policies of two successive governments.
3. I would like to offer a historical _____.
4. We can _____ that the moon will continue to go around the earth until the end of time.
5. The survey found a wide _____ in the prices charged for canteen food.

Group 5

impose	vital	strain	dominate
institution	enterprise	troop	

1. Every year new _____ of influenza develop.
2. Women are no longer _____ by the men in their relationships.
3. The _____ is moving forward to the mountainous area.
4. It was _____ that the elections should be

free of coercion or intimidation.

5. No party may _____ its will on the other party.

Group 6

objective	remarkable	abuse	assess
motion	pitch	episode	

1. By measuring the _____ of the galaxies in a cluster, astronomers can infer the cluster's mass.
2. She suggests you first _____ your income and outgoings.
3. He has displayed _____ courage in his efforts to reform the party.
4. He had no _____ evidence that anything extraordinary was happening.
5. The whole _____ has drawn attention again to internecine strife in the ruling party.

Group 7

plot	trial	capacity	procedure
alter	criterion	retain	

1. The _____ of the novel is intricate and fascinating.
2. Practice is the sole _____ for testing truth.
3. A _____ crowd of 76,000 people was at Wembley football stadium for the event.
4. Diet and exercise will _____ your shape.
5. _____ copies of all correspondence, since you may need them at a later date.

Group 8

implement	extensive	insurance	reference
conservative	appeal	commitment	

1. He summed up his philosophy, with _____ to

Calvin.
2. The blast caused _____ damage to the house.
3. The best _____ for digging a garden is a spade.
4. Occasionally I find the _____ and responsibility daunting.
5. The girl was well dressed, as usual, though in a more _____ style.

Group 9

presence	reserve	trail	expose
cast	eliminate	external	

1. Women tend to attribute their success to _____ causes such as luck.
2. The _____ or absence of clouds can have an important impact on heat transfer.
3. The Gulf has 65 percent of the world's oil _____.
4. No one wants to _____ themselves, lay their feelings bare.
5. America wants to _____ tariffs on items such as electronics.

Group 10

split	estate	plastic	row
protest	emerge	intervention	

1. It caused some _____ and indignation.
2. Mr. Shevardnadze _____ as a major figure in the reform movement.
3. If the chicken is fairly small, you may simply _____ it in half.
4. Prying off the _____ lid, she took out a small scoop.
5. Many people felt he would be hostile to the idea of foreign _____.

Answers — P93

4

Word List 2

Group 1

prompt	gear	resort	transaction
grab	champion	pump	

1. He edged closer to the telephone, ready to _____ it.
2. The strike was _____ by the sacking of a worker.
3. He passionately _____ human rights.
4. He claimed his punishing work schedule had made him _____ to taking the drug.
5. They have made huge profit out of the _____.

Group 2

comprehensive	consensus	stir	panic
passion	mess	reflection	

1. He was educated at a co-ed _____ school.
2. He has a _____ for gambling.
3. There is a broad _____ of opinion about the policies which should be pursued.
4. She was a sensible girl and did not _____.
5. In his latest collection of poems readers are confronted with a series of _____ on death.

Group 3

twist	grin	racial	vessel
tap	seal	rear	

1. Our chemistry teacher _____ all kinds of birds.
2. Heat the _____ and try to blow out the stopper.
3. The body was _____, its legs at an awkward angle.
4. Bobby looked at her with a sheepish _____.
5. _____ discrimination aroused popular indignation and disgust.

Group 4

constitute	exposure	attribute	venture
extract	integration	entity	

1. Steam, water and ice _____ the three phases of the same matter.
2. Don't _____ into the jungle without a guide.
3. The aim is to promote closer economic _____.
4. Don't _____ all your mistakes to obje-ctive causes.
5. _____ of unprotected skin to the sun carries the risk of developing skin cancer.

Group 5

interval	moderate	domain	implementation
controversial	radical	stroke	

1. The _____ of the treaty was obstructed.
2. The Football League has announced its proposals for a _____ reform of the way football is run in England.
3. The ferry service has restarted after an _____ of 12 years.
4. Immigration is a _____ issue in many

countries.

5. _____ exercise will benefit you.

Group 6

parallel	spin	ally	compound
innocent	chamber	interior	

1. This kind of Chinese medicine is a _____ medicine.
2. The Earth _____ on its own axis.
3. The _____ of the house was furnished with heavy, old-fashioned pieces.
4. She will regret losing a close political _____.
5. The police knew from day one that I was _____.

Group 7

acid	reckon	sustain	cluster
inquiry	seminar	stimulate	

1. Toni _____ that it must be about three o'clock.
2. But he has _____ his fierce social conscience from young adulthood through old age.
3. He made some _____ and discovered she had gone to the Continent.
4. Students are asked to prepare material in advance of each weekly _____.
5. The passengers _____ together in small groups.

Group 8

scatter	catalog	narrative	distinct
undergo	beam	render	

1. The detention raised two _____ but closely linked questions.
2. He was a writer of great _____ power.
3. They've been _____ toys everywhere.
4. He had a chance to _____ some service to his country.
5. I hope that I shall never again have to _____ such unpleasant experience.

Group 9

exceed	incentive	exploit	deposit
regulate	trigger	constraint	

1. There is some _____ in the bottom of the flask.
2. His performance _____ all expectations.
3. Competition is a strong _____ to industry.
4. A _____ is a restriction on the degree of freedom you have in providing a solution.
5. It will _____ off a chain reaction.

Group 10

dismiss	subsequent	conscious	theoretical
dynamic	mount	scenario	

1. The _____ of the market demands constant change and adjustment.
2. There was _____ concern in her voice.
3. The book was banned in the US, as were two _____ books.
4. In this _____, we need to detect speculative action in a trade system.
5. I would certainly _____ any allegations of impropriety by the Labor Party.

Answers ⟶ P94

Word List 3

Group 1

aluminum	sensation	partial	collective
specimen	empirical	clip	

1. I do feel deeply the strength of the _____.
2. He managed to reach a _____ agreement with both republics.
3. The pain was so bad that she lost all _____.
4. I saw an old man out _____ his hedge.
5. There is no _____ evidence to support his thesis.

Group 2

embed	confine	spectrum	onset
nucleus	thread	aesthetic	

1. One of the bullets passed through Andrea's chest before _____ itself in a wall.
2. I can't stand the _____ of this marriage.
3. The individual colors within the light _____ are believed to have an effect on health.
4. With the _____ of war, oil prices climbed past $30 a barrel.
5. This time I'll do it properly with a needle and _____.

Group 3

trait	bundle	elaborate	manipulate
metaphor	reinforce	discourse	

1. In poetry the rose is often a _____ for love.
2. They used _____ secret codes, as when the names of trees stood for letters.
3. Your positive response will _____ her actions.
4. Primitive man quickly learned how to _____ tools.
5. This also made him moody and bad-tempered, a _____ that would persist and lose him friends.

Group 4

manual	portray	crude	conceptual
reproduce	spontaneous	particle	

1. A _____ design and cost study was made by TVA for EPA in 1968.
2. To be _____ and careless is an extremely bad style of work.
3. These portraits _____ my attitude to them.
4. He bought a _____ of car repairs.
5. _____ applause broke out as soon as she finished speaking.

Group 5

immune	transmit	commentary	compensate
irrelevant	initiate	conceive	

1. We _____ of the family as being in a constant state of change.
2. His running _____ on the football match was excellent.
3. He _____ his keen enjoyment of singing to the audience.
4. The company agreed to keep up high levels of output in order to _____ for supplies lost.
5. The patient's _____ system would reject the

transplanted organ as a foreign object.

Group 6

projection	magnitude	defect	merge
dialect	slot	vague	

1. A _____ of vision prevented him from focusing accurately.
2. They took me into a _____ room to see a picture.
3. An operation of this _____ is going to be difficult.
4. The two countries _____ into one.
5. Can you tell the difference between Putonghua and Beijing _____?

Group 7

commodity	radiation	dilemma	obscure
resemble	bizarre	magnetic	

1. She describes her own moral _____ in making the film.
2. Many brokers were charged with cheating customers in _____ trades.
3. Don't allow one error to _____ great merits.
4. That just seemed _____ and wrong.
5. We just naturally think that the future will _____ the past.

Group 8

spray	bulk	static	elite
sphere	colonial	undermine	

1. Despite his _____ he moved lightly on his feet.
2. They were, by and large, a very wealthy, privileged _____.

3. Don't view things as _____ and isolated.
4. Drops of blood _____ across the room.
5. This is within his _____ of accountability.

Group 9

intensity	aggregate	ritual	invade
compact	adjacent	diagnose	

1. The whole Italian culture revolves around the _____ of eating.
2. The tax increases will, in the _____, cause much hardship.
3. He sat in an _____ room and waited.
4. We'll wipe out any enemy that dares to _____ our territory.
5. Speech is made up of sound waves that vary in frequency and _____.

Group 10

primitive	basin	implicit	fiber
decay	explicit	fusion	

1. The clue is _____ although he didn't say it.
2. She was a _____ of the dreamer and doer.
3. There is a flood in the river _____ in the South this summer.
4. The ground was scattered with _____ leaves.
5. _____ humans needed to be able to react like this to escape from dangerous animals.

Answers ⟶ P95

Word List 4

Group 1

anniversary	authorize	tactic	bare
approximate	ingredient	provoke	

1. Speed is the essential _____ of all athletics.
2. The _____ could well help invigorate a struggling campaign.
3. The Society is celebrating its tenth _____ this year.
4. That's probably the most _____, bleak, barren and inhospitable island I've ever seen.
5. I will personally _____ the use of force against the consulate.

Group 2

shed	attorney	degrade	elimination
reservoir	terminology	generous	

1. The _____ of all nuclear weapons would make the world a safer place.
2. This dictionary provides the precise definitions needed to use embedded systems _____ properly.
3. Torrents of water gushed into the _____.
4. In sound recording, interference, such as ambient noise and reverberation, _____ the quality.
5. We had a long meeting with the _____ general.

Group 3

spark	altitude	optical	radius

atomic	cease	violate	

1. Each _____ cluster is made up of neutrons and protons.
2. The mountain has an _____ of 1,500 meters.
3. He has _____ trouble.
4. A dropped cigarette may have _____ the fire.
5. They agreed on a _____ fire.

Group 4

patch	vulnerable	counterpart	accommodate
enclose	uplift	descend	

1. Their tanks would be _____ to attack from the air.
2. Things are cooler and damper as we _____ to the cellar.
3. There was a small _____ of blue in the grey clouds.
4. We _____ our visiting scholars with new apartments.
5. The Foreign Secretary telephoned his Italian _____ to protest.

Group 5

prayer	exclusive	predator	compel
contradictory	inevitable	thermal	

1. I felt morally _____ to help.
2. They both have learnt that ambition and successful fatherhood can be mutually _____.
3. This scarcity is _____ in less developed

countries.

4. The arrival of this South American _____ threatened the survival of native species.
5. It is _____ between people's profits and nature.

Group 6

halt	contradict	fracture	withdrawal
patent	arbitrary	mainstream	

1. The result seems to _____ a major U.S. study reported last November.
2. He held a number of _____ for his many innovations.
3. They insisted upon a _____ of the statement and a public apology.
4. Exports have not been _____ completely because another line is operational.
5. His conduct appears to have been _____ and harsh.

Group 7

priest	reception	diminish	acceleration
overlook	steer	dawn	

1. We _____ all sorts of warning signals about our own health.
2. This could mean _____ public support for the war.
3. He has also called for an _____ of political reforms.
4. At the _____ they served smoked salmon.
5. The enemy opened fire on our lines at early _____.

Group 8

designate	sculpture	desperate	flee
resume	plausible	devastate	

1. Exciting artistic breakthroughs have recently occurred in the fields of painting, _____ and architecture.
2. Some of the rooms were _____ as offices.
3. I decided not to abandon John when he was in such a _____ position.
4. This reasoning, though _____, is incorrect.
5. He _____ to Costa Rica to avoid military service.

Group 9

retreat	companion	sediment	torture
velocity	proton	rage	

1. The French, suddenly outnumbered, were forced to _____.
2. He was a charming travelling _____.
3. A bullet goes from this gun with a _____ of 3000 feet per second.
4. This _____ will then probably be formed into a folded and imbricate structure.
5. As the evening progressed, sadness turned to _____.

Group 10

founder	friction	gauge	deem
trivial	formulation	integrity	

1. Try to _____ its weight.
2. Oil is put in machinery to reduce the _____.
3. He's a man of _____, and can be trusted.
4. He was one of the _____ of the school's medical faculty.
5. I _____ it my duty to remind her of it.

Answers — P96

Word List 5

Group 1

suspicious	deliberate	exaggerate	appall
vanish	exotic	fierce	

1. Many of these species have _____ or are facing extinction.
2. This can happen for a variety of reasons, and these reasons can be unintended as well as _____.
3. Find out which of these are native plants and which are _____.
4. We were instructed to report any _____ activity in the neighborhood.
5. It _____ me to think of the way those children have been abused.

Group 2

biography	haul	timber	hybrid
parade	drown	anchor	

1. After the team won the championship, the city threw a _____ for them.
2. The roots _____ the plant in the earth.
3. The loud music _____ the sound of their conversation.
4. Spanish and English have mixed with each other in the United States to create a _____ language.
5. The car was _____ away to the junkyard.

Group 3

delicate	speculate	aspiration	inherent

predecessor	confrontation	expedition	

1. Today's computers are much faster than their _____ were.
2. She left home with _____ for a better life.
3. We want cooperation, not _____.
4. We don't know what happened—we can only _____.
5. The tomb was adorned with _____ carvings.

Group 4

respective	maneuver	dwell	soar
hop	testify	offset	

1. These statistics _____ that the program is working.
2. "I'd rather not _____ on the past," he told me.
3. Gains in one area _____ losses in another.
4. Steve and I were at very different stages in our _____ careers.
5. It took seven people to _____ the tiger out of its cage.

Group 5

chop	flock	distract	distort
cautious	persistent	interference	

1. The scientists are _____ about using enzyme therapy on humans.
2. The local story _____ attention from news of the war overseas.
3. That salesman was _____ in asking me to buy a car.
4. The odd camera angle _____ her figure in

the photograph.
5. It was hard to hear the radio program because of all the _____.

Group 6

intact	chaos	illuminate	soak
receipt	conjunction	unfold	

1. Customs men put dynamite in the water to destroy the cargo, but most of it was left _____.
2. Instead of formulas and charts, the two instructors use games and drawings to _____ their subject.
3. The loss of electricity caused _____ throughout the city.
4. Textbooks are designed to be used in _____ with classroom teaching.
5. The outcome depends on conditions as well as how events _____.

Group 7

lawn	arch	succession	verdict
compile	summon	flush	

1. She is now seventh in line of _____ to the throne.
2. It often takes five or six years of hard work to _____ a good dictionary.
3. The jury returned a unanimous guilty _____.
4. He _____ his subordinates hastily to his office.
5. He _____ with embarrassment.

Group 8

penetrate	postpone	wreck	verify
fetch	cling	grind	

1. The baseball game was _____ until tomorrow because of rain.
2. Later, findings _____ the scientist's theory.
3. X-rays can _____ many objects.
4. Many houses were _____ by the hurricane.
5. Most of the wheat will be _____ into flour.

Group 9

shatter	trunk	intimate	immense
furnish	disposal	restraint	

1. He has enough money to _____ the apartment nicely.
2. This is mainly due to the improper _____ of rubbish by people.
3. They remained _____ friends throughout their lives.
4. The president calls for spending _____ in some areas.
5. His dreams were _____ by their rejection.

Group 10

cathedral	inspect	contend	smash
passionate	entrepreneur	stiff	

1. She had the car _____ by a mechanic before she bought it.
2. These people _____ that they have earned the right to the land.
3. This is too _____. I can't bend it with my hands.
4. An _____ is a person who sets up businesses and business deals.
5. He _____ the vase with a hammer.

Answers ---- P97

12

Word List 6

Group 1

descent	chorus	invoke	imperative

disperse	consecutive	provincial	

1. The team's winning streak has lasted for seven _____ games.
2. She considers it a moral _____ to help people in need.
3. She _____ history to prove her point.
4. Police fired shots and used tear gas to _____ the demonstrators.
5. She is too _____ to try foreign foods.

Group 2

gorgeous	drawback	brew	fuss

blaze	revival	skeptical	

1. The cosmetics industry uses _____ women to sell its skincare products.
2. This return to realism has produced a _____ of interest in a number of artists.
3. When I said I'd finished my homework early, Mom looked _____.
4. He felt the apartment's only _____ was that it was too small.
5. Some 4,000 firefighters are battling the _____.

Group 3

prone	shrine	envy	feasible

rib	abolish	supreme	

1. The government is looking for a _____ way to create new jobs.
2. He is in favor of _____ the death penalty.
3. Their exotic vacations inspired _____ in their friends.
4. For all her experience as a television reporter, she was still _____ to camera nerves.
5. Her approval was of _____ importance.

Group 4

endanger	discard	prose	civic

saint	embody	plague	

1. They must _____ their ideas in sub-stantial institutions if they are to survive.
2. Read the manufacturer's guidelines before _____ the box.
3. Recent improvements to the downtown area are a point of _____ pride.
4. The severe drought has _____ crops throughout the area.
5. Computer viruses _____ Internet users.

Group 5

ceramic	mansion	heap	entail

volatile	intensify	cushion	

1. They _____ their efforts to increase sales.
2. There is a _____ of old newspapers.
3. We didn't have a financial _____ when my husband lost his job.
4. There have been riots before and the situation is _____.
5. A lavish wedding _____ extensive planning and often staggering expense.

Group 6

transparent	bud	vest	intake

portable	excursion	furious	

1. She's _____ at how slowly the investigation is proceeding.
2. You should limit your daily _____ of fats and sugars.
3. A _____ machine or device is designed to be easily carried or moved.
4. We had one last trip to make a _____ from Damascus by car.
5. The company has to make its accounts and operations as _____ as possible.

Group 7

choke	buffer	debris	bulb

robust	compatible	vacant	

1. He was always the _____ one, physically strong and mentally sharp.
2. Chew your food well; don't _____.
3. After the earthquake, rescuers began digging through the _____ in search of survivors.
4. This printer is _____ with most PCs.
5. The seat was left _____ when the secretary resigned.

Group 8

adhere	indulge	recount	crisp

canvas	notorious	pirate	

1. All members of the association _____ to a strict code of practice.
2. Bake the potatoes for 15 minutes, till they're nice and _____.
3. The lawyer has defended some of the most _____ criminals.
4. He then _____ the story of the interview for his first job.
5. It's my birthday. I'm going to _____ myself and eat whatever I want to eat.

Group 9

stab	purse	elicit	splash

denounce	underestimate	posture	

1. Never _____ the importance of a good education.
2. He dropped the bottle and water _____ onto the floor.
3. She's trying to _____ the support of other committee members.
4. The government called on the group to _____ the use of violence.
5. A good upright _____ will prevent back-aches.

Group 10

disastrous	expire	skull	plow

municipal	fertilizer	frown	

1. The bad weather could have a _____ effect on the area's tourism industry.
2. The boss just stood there and _____ at his assistant who, once again, was in trouble.
3. He had lived illegally in the United States for five years after his visitor's visa _____.
4. We use organic _____ in our gardens.
5. _____ means associated with or belonging to a city or town that has its own local government.

Answers — P98

Word List 7

Group 1

contaminate	extinction	culminate	solitary

transit	moisture	congestion

1. The loggers say their jobs are faced with _____ because of declining timber sales.
2. She had been held in _____ confinement for four months.
3. These chemicals _____ water and poison animals.
4. Some of the party's luggage is lost in _____.
5. All his efforts _____ in selling the house.

Group 2

collision	narrator	expel	gasp

eternal	bustle	gravel

1. The play represents the _____ of three generations.
2. Whoever believes in Him shall have _____ life.
3. They were told at first that they should simply _____ the refugees.
4. She gave a small _____ of pain.
5. They find only irony in the _____ concern.

Group 3

enlist	dinosaur	veil	recur

fertile	hamper	frost

1. Three thousand men were _____.
2. Most roses like a sunny position in a fairly _____ soil.
3. These could only have been made after the _____ was dead.
4. She swathes her face in a _____ of decorative muslin.
5. My grandmother's illness is likely to _____.

Group 4

duplicate	tangle	cramp	stationary

unveil	defy	equate

1. Criminals _____ the law.
2. This property eliminates all _____ documents.
3. The themes get _____ in Mr. Mahfouz's epic storytelling.
4. I wanted the video to slowly _____ the progress and rhythm of their construction.
5. One should not _____ wealth with happiness.

Group 5

quarterback	cripple	applaud	descendant

prosperous	humiliate	alienate

1. The audience laughed and _____.
2. She has gone from being a healthy, fit and sporty young woman to being a _____.
3. They are the _____ of plants imported by the early settlers.
4. She had been beaten and _____ by her husband.
5. This district is getting more and more _____ and bustling.

Group 6

empower	nun	stereo	erupt

spacious	comprehend	drastic	

1. A _____ reformation of the present housing system has been carried out.
2. Then, without warning, she _____ into laughter.
3. The rooms were _____, with tall windows and high ceilings.
4. In Kenya, reforestation project helps increase food supply, build skills and income, and _____ women.
5. If you can use a word correctly and effectively, you _____ it.

Group 7

autobiography	exploitation	void	coral

formidable	discern	ditch	

1. Some people find it difficult to _____ blue from green.
2. He fronted a _____ band of fighters.
3. _____ was written late in life.
4. Serious waste and environmental pollution still exist in the _____ and utilization of mineral resources.
5. The agreement will be considered null and _____.

Group 8

potent	parasite	advent	categorize

crust	odor	compress	

1. I was convinced by his _____ arguments.
2. Swallows come by group at the _____ of spring.

3. This mirrors the way we _____ things in the real world.
4. Air will _____ but the brake fluid won't.
5. A colorless and clear liquid with characteristic flavor and _____.

Group 9

submarine	theatrical	prevalent	stove

census	clan	dispense	

1. In a _____ gesture Glass clamped his hand over his eyes.
2. This condition is more _____ in women than in men.
3. The Union had already _____ £ 40,000 in grants.
4. _____ earthquakes often happen in ocean.
5. According to the latest _____, our population has increased.

Group 10

excerpt	apparatus	commute	diplomacy

intimacy	blink	overtake	

1. You know that the _____, between you and my husband, has caused me a lot of pain.
2. One of the boys had to be rescued by firemen wearing breathing _____.
3. It was all over in the _____ of an eye.
4. I have included an _____ from the article, and we can all learn from this example.
5. The talks have now gone into a stage of quiet _____.

Answers — P99

Word List 8

Group 1

inhale	shortcoming	apprentice	hinder

deception	sprout	envision

1. A thigh injury increasingly _____ her mobility.
2. Marriages usually break down as a result of the _____ of both partners.
3. She denies obtaining a pecuniary advantage by _____.
4. It's not quite a year since she became an _____.
5. _____ quickly, then bring your head and chest back down and continue the body undulations.

Group 2

flake	inclusive	recreational	impetus

propel	chaotic	eradicate

1. It was a shooting star that _____ me into astronomy in the first place.
2. The town and its environs are inviting, with _____ attractions and art museums.
3. Training will commence on 5 October, running from Tuesday to Saturday _____.
4. Innovation is the main _____ and source to cultivate and promote enterprise's core competitive ability.
5. My own house feels as filthy and _____ as a bus terminal.

Group 3

indispensable	unravel	attic	vicinity

commend	authoritative	greed

1. A young mother flew to Iceland to _____ the mystery of her husband's disappearance.
2. This earthquake affected several cities in the _____.
3. He has a commanding presence and deep, _____ voice.
4. The family is the _____ part in the process of the development and construction of human society.
5. _____ is a bottomless hole which can never be filled.

Group 4

abrupt	renewable	communal	intrinsic

glacier	compass	capsule

1. The _____ and extrinsic causes of splice loss for optical fiber are analyzed and summarized in detail.
2. Mullins knocked me off-balance with his _____ change of subject.
3. A party of people assembled to promote sociability and _____ activity.
4. They sailed across the Baltic and North Seas with only a _____ to guide them.
5. The company engaged in research and development of new energy and _____ fuels.

Group 5

bleach	eclipse	heed	allude

contamination	catalyst	lava

1. I cautioned him many times but he paid no _____.
2. The negative intense emotion is the University student's _____ of the intense emotional criminal offence.
3. Remove stains by soaking in a mild solution of _____.
4. The gramophone had been _____ by new technology such as the compact disc.
5. Some people are still suffering ill effects from the _____ of their water.

Group 6

granite	coil	hazardous	ruthless
diffuse	cache	backdrop	

1. Passive smoking can be _____ to health.
2. They represented a _____ and illegitimate regime that could not remain forever.
3. The profits rise was achieved against a _____ of falling metal prices.
4. _____ is a very hard stone.
5. _____ the fiber into a helix.

Group 7

gland	coarse	immerse	perennial
excavate	superiority	reclaim	

1. They all _____ in the beautiful music.
2. He set him on the bed and rubbed him down with a _____ towel.
3. They realized it would be suicidal to resist in the face of overwhelming military _____.
4. A _____ is a plant that lives indefinitely.
5. They plan to _____ a large hole before putting in the foundations.

Group 8

mute	crater	visualize	adjoin
entice	attest	earnest	

1. I can't bear my deaf and _____ English.
2. Canada and United States _____.
3. He can _____ to the divine one's generosity.
4. There are several things you can do to _____ more customers to buy from you.
5. Susan _____ her wedding day and saw herself walking down the aisle on her father's arm.

Group 9

withstand	deterioration	anomaly	frenzy
decease	evaporate	gigantic	

1. The British public's wariness of opera is an _____ in Europe.
2. They can _____ extremes of temperature and weather without fading or cracking.
3. Blasting cold air over it makes the water _____.
4. In a _____ of hate he killed his enemy.
5. The changes to the country's economy have resulted in a sharp _____ in people's standard of living.

Group 10

occupant	mitigate	imprint	canyon
chore	discredit	condense	

1. He had plenty of feedback and plenty of time to _____ this issue, but he can be stubborn.
2. Most of the _____ had left before the fire broke out.
3. I find writing reports a real _____.
4. The ground still bore the _____ of their feet.
5. They spread disinformation in order to _____ politicians.

Answers → P100

Word List 9

Group 1

paramount	visionary	petal	pivotal

disarm	aquatic	overshadow	

1. He was always _____ by his brilliant elder brother.
2. The _____ goal is to restore the colonial-era house with complete historical accuracy.
3. He has a lifelong fascination with sharks and other fearsome _____ creatures.
4. The report was missing a _____ piece of information.
5. She is known as a _____ leader.

Group 2

dignify	permeate	insulate	intersect

paraphrase	pessimistic	carnival	

1. The delicious smell emanating from the kitchen _____ the entire house.
2. They _____ their departure with a ceremony.
3. He has an extremely negative and _____ attitude.
4. Your essays on human rights should have some original thought and not be simply _____ of what's in the textbook.
5. They used a special type of fiberglass to _____ the attic.

Group 3

recourse	asteroid	transient	neutralize

shun	constellation	colonize	

1. Their happiness was _____, for the war broke out soon after they got married.
2. Weeds quickly _____ the field.
3. The public believes its only _____ is to take to the streets.
4. After his divorce he found himself being _____ by many of his former friends.
5. An acid is _____ with lime.

Group 4

ridicule	tidal	nourish	culprit

converse	vigor	camouflage	

1. The animal blends in with the sand, so it's _____ from predator birds above.
2. What is one of the most common greenhouse gases in our atmosphere, one of the major _____ in global warming?
3. President Clinton displayed no lack of _____ when he began to speak.
4. The other kids _____ him for the way he dressed.
5. We need good food to _____ the starving infants.

Group 5

sterile	formative	incompetent	negligible

touchdown	deduce	integer	

1. A _____ amount of damage was done to the vehicle.
2. I can _____ from the simple observation of your behavior that you're trying to hide

something from me.

3. The astronauts are preparing for _____ tomorrow morning.

4. _____ couples sometimes choose to adopt needy children.

5. The defendant was declared _____ to stand trial.

Group 6

perish	hardy	agreeable	intrude
improvise	feasibility	dissolution	

1. The plants form a kind of colony, a community that will thrive and _____ together.
2. I doubt the _____ of the plan.
3. Would I be _____ if I came along with you?
4. I then begin to _____ melodies vocally.
5. I've gone out of my way to be _____ to his friends.

Group 7

analogous	additive	impoverish	perimeter
wane	requisite	conformity	

1. The moon is _____.
2. She has now become a widow who had been _____ by inflation.
3. A university degree has become _____ for any successful career in this field.
4. Most teenagers feel pressure to _____.
5. Sleep has often been thought of as being in some way _____ to death.

Group 8

chronological	submerge	myriad	numb
rectangular	courageous	latitude	

1. There are _____ of stars in the Milky Way.
2. He was the only one who was _____ enough to step out of hiding.
3. A stroke can cause one side of your body to go _____.
4. The story is told in a linear and _____ order.
5. We weren't given much _____ in deciding how to do the job.

Group 9

plumb	retard	primate	overhear
mania	hasten	encyclopedia	

1. Stress chemicals can _____ ageing.
2. I _____ a rumor about you.
3. He is a scientist who spent her life _____ the minds of criminals.
4. The problems have _____ the progress of the program.
5. She would typically experience a period of _____ and then suddenly become deeply depressed.

Group 10

thaw	extravagant	cosmopolitan	burrow
furnace	bland	explanatory	

1. Greater cultural diversity has led to a more _____ attitude among the town's younger generations.
2. Plant the seeds in early spring as soon as the ground _____.
3. I hope the graphs on the following pages are self-_____.
4. The film is notable for its _____ settings and special effects.
5. The vegetable soup was rather _____.

Answers → P101

20

Word List 10

Group 1

durability	tyrant	delineate	diligent
fidelity	exhale	deviate	

1. In her speech she _____ the city plan with great care.
2. Nylons have the virtue of _____.
3. The airplane's route _____ from the flight plan.
4. Dogs are famous for their _____.
5. He enhanced the endowment by _____ study in high school.

Group 2

alight	improbable	ancestry	tranquil
hind	entangle	emblem	

1. He was described as a _____, calm person.
2. Don't _____ the fishing lines.
3. Frogs have long _____ legs.
4. A flock of eight swans circled above, then _____ on the pond.
5. She claims to be able to trace her _____ all the way back to the earliest settlers.

Group 3

immortal	desolate	grandiose	recital
arduous	proverb	colossal	

1. Our mortal bodies are inhabited by _____ souls.

2. The refugees made an _____ journey through the mountains.
3. Even by modern standards, the 46, 000 ton Titanic was a _____ ship.
4. The house was _____, ready to be torn down.
5. She is going to give a piano _____.

Group 4

unforeseen	drench	surmise	decipher
grandeur	insightful	repel	

1. His _____ proved correct.
2. He met a _____ of rain.
3. Unfortunately, due to _____ circumstances, this year's show has been cancelled.
4. She offered some interesting, _____ observations.
5. Like poles _____, unlike poles attract.

Group 5

exertion	sporadic	decompose	illiterate
coerce	pictorial	rudimentary	

1. He has only a _____ knowledge of the subject.
2. Clark had somehow been able to _____ Jenny into doing whatever he told her to do.
3. He _____ considerable influence on the thinking of the scientific community on these issues.
4. There are still many _____ people in our country.
5. As the waste materials _____, they produce methane gas.

Group 6

amphibian	clam	cello	reassess
abdomen	atlas	aria	

1. The _____ is a member of the violin family.
2. Both the toad and frog are _____.
3. The _____ contains forty maps, including three of Great Britain.
4. The patient is complaining of pain in the _____.
5. It is time to _____ your relationship with your parents.

Group 7

heyday	decimal	meticulous	edible
eject	inconclusive	nibble	

1. I find the evidence _____.
2. He is a _____ manager, a manager par excellence.
3. By the 80s, punk rock had really had its _____.
4. This safety invention will _____ the pilot from a burning plane.
5. The food at the hotel was barely _____.

Group 8

leftover	gist	encroach	candid
pristine	mutate	aromatic	

1. New housing is starting to _____ upon the surrounding fields.
2. Scientists have found a genetic _____ that appears to be the cause of Huntington's disease.
3. Now the house is in _____ condition.
4. _____ food and unwashed dishes cover the dirty counters.
5. He was quite _____ about the way the case had been handled.

Group 9

carbonate	exemplary	celestial	divisive
luminous	mystify	perpendicular	

1. Her behavior was _____.
2. Abortion has always been a _____ issue.
3. He has done more to confuse and _____ the subject than to clear it up.
4. Stars are _____ bodies.
5. The desert was _____, starkly beautiful.

Group 10

embellish	neurological	perplex	fragrant
allusion	intermittent	helium	

1. This problem is hard enough to _____ even the teacher.
2. Just tell the truth and don't _____ the story by any means.
3. It's a cold night here, with _____ rain showers and a blustery wind.
4. His statement was seen as an _____ to the recent drug-related killings.
5. There are also serious _____ complications.

Answers — P102

Word List 11

Group 1

inquisitive	overuse	Antarctica	make up
amusing	pile up	artificial	

1. Young children sometimes _____ 'and' in their writing.
2. His poems reveal an intensely _____ and curious mind.
3. The city is dotted with small lakes, natural and _____.
4. Problems were _____ at work.
5. Ozone damages the cellular _____ of plants and trees.

Group 2

inadvertent	reducible	interstellar	elliptical
give rise to	arid	argumentative	

1. He was pardoned for _____ mans-laughter.
2. The elements become part of the _____ gas and dust in the universe.
3. The plant has adapted to the _____ environment in desert.
4. The new law _____ a lot of complaints.
5. The moon follows an _____ path around the Earth.

Group 3

life span	guarded	soundproof	coating
geothermal	conductive	heredity	

1. The rehearsal room is well _____.

2. He has given a _____ and conservative welcome to the idea.
3. Salt water is much more _____ than fresh water is.
4. _____ is an important factor in causing the cancer.
5. They have extended the potential _____ of humanity everywhere.

Group 4

slip into	take into account	cosmology	blemish
enliven	permeable	deprive of	

1. We'll have to _____ what the room will be mainly used for when we do the design.
2. A series of burn marks _____ the table's surface.
3. The rain _____ through the soil.
4. _____ is the study of the origin, evolution, and eventual fate of the universe.
5. Working those long hours was _____ him of his sleep.

Group 5

ecologist	biased	zenith	vertebra
constrict	interracial	complicated	

1. He is now at the _____ of his powers.
2. He is too _____ to write about the case objectively.
3. He felt _____ by their notions of what was proper.
4. The game's rules are too _____.
5. _____ marriages can cause many problems within the family.

Group 6

rapidity	orbital	enigma	nourishment
diffidence	put off	arise from	

1. Why she quit the team is an _____ to me.
2. The _____ with which she can do mental math calculations is amazing.
3. We were _____ by the book's abusive tone.
4. With encouragement he became less _____.
5. The Moon _____ the Earth.

Group 7

overwhelming	traceable	nomad	by-product
put up with	refer to	devastate	

1. The word "amiable" _____ back to the Latin word for "friend".
2. She was _____ by a sense of tragedy.
3. Try not to _____ the recent death of her aunt.
4. They had _____ behavior from their son which they would not have tolerated from anyone else.
5. Raised in a _____ family, she attended half a dozen different high schools.

Group 8

exacting	fragility	bemoan	reciprocate
ethic	idealist	in terms of	

1. Karen had done her bit for me, and I was more than happy to _____.
2. Some critics are always _____ the state of the language.
3. He thinks of everything _____ money.
4. He was shocked when his normally _____ supervisor complimented him on a job well done.
5. She is devastated and is now in an emotionally _____ state.

Group 9

outgrowth	upend	photosynthesis	enduring
discoloration	malnourishment	inhospitable	

1. Last time we talked about _____, the process by which plants use light to convert carbon dioxide and water into food.
2. In a country that once fed the world, children were dying of _____.
3. A predictable _____ of the suburb's ever growing population will be the need for more schools.
4. It's very _____ of him to be so rude to strangers.
5. This chance meeting was the start of an _____ friendship.

Group 10

deprecate	telling	resourceful	symbiosis
fixed	dramatize	marshland	

1. He proves to be _____, and clever in dealing with problems.
2. That day remains _____ in my memory.
3. She cited a series of statistics to _____ the seriousness of the problem.
4. Movie critics tried to outdo one another in _____ the comedy as the stupidest movie of the year.
5. Her experience is a _____ example of why the nation's educational system needs to be changed.

Answers ⟶ P103

基本级 Level 2

1 仅仅完成单词认知往往不能转化为分数的提升；因此强烈建议考生重视这份结合语境与单词
   运用的配套练习。

2 基本级练习与基本级词表同步完成，建议每完成一个 List 的记忆之后就完成相应练习。

3 每份练习包含 10 组"7 选 5 句子填空"；考生可以先将 7 个单词的中文意思填在单词下方
   的方框里，再根据上下文，在句子的空格处填入最恰当的单词。

4 所有练习皆配有答案。

Word List 1

Group 1

precipitate	complement	optimal	discrete

substitution	converge	transition	

1. The two roads _____ in the center of town.
2. He keeps his engine tuned for _____ performance.
3. minerals _____ from seawater
4. the difficult _____ from childhood to adulthood
5. The scarf is a perfect _____ to her outfit.

Group 2

tragedy	boost	allege	paradox

veteran	array	enzyme	

1. It is a _____ that computers need maintenance so often, since they are meant to save people time.
2. Exercise can sometimes provide a _____ of energy.
3. an _____ of solar panels
4. He _____ that the mayor has accepted bribes.
5. a _____ of two world wars

Group 3

intervene	simulate	equity	liberal

keen	novice	stereotype	

1. The military had to _____ to restore order.
2. In making these decisions we should be governed by the principle of _____.
3. a book for the _____ chess player
4. The model will be used to _____ the effects of an earthquake.
5. It's not fair to _____ a group of people based on one person you don't like.

Group 4

competent	articulate	chromosome	cater

conservation	pragmatic	defect	

1. She specializes in the _____ of furniture.
2. She's an intelligent and _____ speaker.
3. They examine their products for _____.
4. A local restaurant _____ the banquet.
5. His _____ view of public education comes from years of working in city schools.

Group 5

parenthesis	allocate	ultimate	senator

censor	correspondence	profound	

1. Sometimes there is little _____ between the way a word is spelled and the way it is pronounced in English.
2. His paintings have had a _____ effect on her own work.
3. Our _____ aim is to increase production.
4. Money from the sale of the house was _____ to each of the children.
5. Government _____ deleted all references to the protest.

Group 6

cruise	descendant	hawk	facet
distress	scandal	composite	

1. Many people in this area are _____ of German immigrants.
2. The gossip magazine is filled with rumors and _____.
3. Each _____ of the problem requires careful attention.
4. The patient showed no obvious signs of _____.
5. The movie's special effects included the use of many _____ photographs.

Group 7

swell	ideology	hedge	contour
susceptible	variant	sweep	

1. the _____ of a totalitarian society
2. He loved the sleek _____ of the car.
3. The virus can infect _____ individuals.
4. A new _____ of the disease appeared.
5. The population has _____ in recent years.

Group 8

dedicate	mentor	elegant	premise
peripheral	rational	protest	

1. A young attorney has decided to _____ her career to helping the poor receive justice.
2. If we focus too much on _____ issues, we will lose sight of the goal.
3. After college, her professor became her close friend and _____.
4. Human beings are _____ creatures capable of sound reasoning.
5. She is the most _____ and gorgeous First Lady in the nation's history.

Group 9

unintelligible	prescribe	prejudice	dominant
tendency	epidemic	merit	

1. The study has no scientific _____ and thus deserves little attention.
2. The organization fights against racial _____.
3. The economy has shown a general _____ toward inflation.
4. The regulations _____ that all employees must pass a physical examination.
5. Dolphin sounds are _____ to humans.

Group 10

testimony	consent	rumor	chronic
monopoly	watershed	transcribe	

1. There were contradictions in her _____.
2. He suffers from _____ arthritis.
3. A _____ moment in her life came when she inherited a reasonable sum of money and was able to start her own coffee shop.
4. The government passed laws intended to break up _____ and so as to bring more players into business.
5. He was reluctant at first but finally _____.

Answers — P104

Word List 2

Group 1

cult	breach	miserable	slaughter
disclosure	superb	warrant	

1. We demand full _____ of the facts.
2. All civilized nations should protest this senseless and inhumane _____.
3. It is feared that he has joined a network of Satan-worshiping _____.
4. This is clearly a _____ of the treaty.
5. My boss is making my life thoroughly _____ with her constant demands and criticism.

Group 2

heritage	jurisdiction	subscription	persistent
warranty	patrol	benchmark	

1. The guard makes a _____ of the building every hour.
2. We were nagged by a _____ salesman.
3. You won't find this magazine at newsstands. It's sold only by _____.
4. This farm is my _____ from my father, as it was for him from his father.
5. This prize-winning biography will be the _____ against which all others will be judged in future years.

Group 3

faction	exile	contingent	splendid
vicious	deploy	vendor	

1. They plan to _____ more American soldiers over the next six months.
2. The president chose to live as _____ rather than face persecution.
3. I know you're upset with her, but there's no need to be _____.
4. Several _____ within the environmental movement have joined forces to save this wilderness area.
5. We have a _____ opportunity to do something really useful.

Group 4

vocal	affiliate	escort	affection
memoir	disguise	flourish	

1. He tried to _____ his voice on the phone but I could tell it was him.
2. The bombers were protected by a fighter _____.
3. Plants and animals _____ here thousands of years ago.
4. Beethoven's ninth symphony has both _____ and instrumental parts.
5. Their group does not _____ itself with any political party.

Group 5

legacy	verge	prohibit	aftermath
enact	mock	assertion	

1. He _____ art only because he doesn't understand it.
2. The suspect was on the _____ of confessing when the officers realized that he hadn't been read his rights.

3. The rules _____ dating a coworker.
4. She left us a _____ of a million dollars.
5. The surgery was successful, but she now had to deal with its _____; a huge bill.

Group 6

heir	arc	accountable	spit
bureau	haunt	clash	

1. He _____ out his piece of coconut.
2. The gray lady _____ the chapel.
3. Police and protesters _____ yesterday.
4. If anything goes wrong, I will hold you personally _____!
5. the Federal _____ of Investigation

Group 7

caution	contempt	fluctuate	reconcile
archive	grief	demographic	

1. You should use _____ when operating the electric saw.
2. His popularity has _____ during his term in office.
3. He feels that wealthy people view him with _____ because he is poor.
4. It can be difficult to _____ your ideals with reality.
5. The _____ information shows that the population increased but the average income went down.

Group 8

utter	batter	despair	crawl
hazard	contemplate	weep	

1. The soldiers _____ forward on their bellies.
2. Things look bad now, but don't _____.

3. The tumbledown old barn was considered a fire _____.
4. She _____ a cry of pleasure.
5. He _____ the meaning of the poem for a long time.

Group 9

outrage	partisan	intimidate	mighty
dread	premature	animate	

1. The barbarians faced a _____ army which seemed so formidable.
2. Many furious people expressed _____ at the court's decision.
3. You shouldn't allow his reputation to _____ you.
4. The film's realistic dinosaurs were _____ on computers.
5. Her _____ death at age 30 stunned her family and friends.

Group 10

generic	dim	amend	compliment
roar	bypass	thrust	

1. The doctor _____ the needle into the patient's arm.
2. Chevre is a _____ term for all goat's milk cheese.
3. We heard a lion _____ in the distance.
4. The bridge is being rebuilt, so we'll have to take the _____.
5. The latest setback has _____ hopes of an early settlement.

Answers → P105

Word List 3

Group 1

badge	turmoil	excavation	wary
eccentric	confer	reiterate	

1. The country has been in _____ for the past 10 years.
2. Moves were made to _____ an honorary degree on her.
3. He was a kind but _____ man, a weirdo as people call him.
4. She avoided answering our questions directly, instead _____ that the answers could be found in her book.
5. Investors are increasingly _____ about putting money into stocks.

Group 2

charitable	aspire	supplementary	shuffle
sob	hover	catastrophe	

1. We never thought that we might _____ to those heights.
2. He _____ across the floor.
3. Bees _____ around the hive.
4. She makes a _____ donation every year.
5. Experts fear a humanitarian _____ if food isn't delivered to the refugees.

Group 3

insane	sensor	exclaim	nuance
hypothetical	literal	linkage	

1. The murderer without an identifiable motivation was found to be _____.
2. We talked about what we would do in various _____ emergencies.
3. She _____ in delight over the Christmas tree.
4. He listened to the subtle _____ in the song.
5. Experts found _____ between population growth and disease.

Group 4

moan	wedge	imminent	appliance
prestigious	ambiguous	relish	

1. We are awaiting their _____ arrival.
2. A nutritional study has been published by a _____ medical journal.
3. He took particular _____ in pointing out my error.
4. We were confused by the _____ wording of the message.
5. All household _____ are now on sale.

Group 5

ponder	larva	menace	souvenir
dissent	mourn	deter	

1. Some potential buyers will be _____ by the price.
2. He _____ the question before he answered.
3. The _____ of a butterfly is called a caterpillar.
4. The Supreme Court, with two justices _____, ruled that the law was constitutional.

5. She could hear the _____ in his voice, threatening he would not just stop.

Group 6

intercept	rehearse	dismay	sober
miniature	gleam	segregate	

1. The civil rights movement fought against practices that _____ blacks and whites.
2. Detectives have been _____ her mail.
3. Her choice of career _____ her parents.
4. He saw the _____ of a flashlight in the distance.
5. I'm driving, so I have to stay _____ tonight.

Group 7

resent	liaison	congress	tangible
ascend	preoccupy	console	

1. They watched their balloons slowly _____ into the sky.
2. She _____ being told what to do.
3. She acts as a _____ between the police department and city schools.
4. Nothing could _____ her after his death.
5. There is no _____ evidence to support her claim.

Group 8

recollection	immunity	abide	proximity
rim	cumulative	decree	

1. I would _____ by their decision.
2. The _____ of the curtains to the fireplace was a cause of concern for the safety inspector.
3. They have developed _____ to the virus.
4. He had a _____ weight gain of 20 pounds over the course of a year.

5. The President issued a _____ making the day a national holiday.

Group 9

stationary	baseline	skepticism	convene
cynical	temperament	sprawl	

1. The two women look alike but are opposite in _____.
2. A car collided with a _____ vehicle.
3. The experiment is meant only to provide a _____ for other studies.
4. We _____ at the hotel for a seminar.
5. The kids _____ on the floor to watch TV.

Group 10

despise	petty	upbringing	speculative
dire	glamorous	acclaim	

1. She looked _____ in her formal black gown.
2. His conclusions are highly _____.
3. My behavior was _____ and stupid. I apologize.
4. The circumstances are now more _____ than ever.
5. He is _____ for being selfish.

Answers — P106

Word List 4

Group 1

affinity	anguish	climax	nostalgia
salvage	jeopardize	precursor	

1. He experienced the _____ of divorce after 10 years of marriage.
2. The wrecked ship was beyond _____.
3. A wave of _____ swept over me when I saw my childhood home.
4. His health has been _____ by poor nutrition.
5. He never felt any _____ with the other kids in his neighborhood.

Group 2

benign	herald	disgrace	transcend
bewilder	provisional	underscore	

1. We were happy to hear that the tumor was _____.
2. The early flowers are _____ of spring.
3. Beethoven's symphonies are music that _____ cultural boundaries.
4. The change in policy seems to have _____ many of our customers.
5. Many feel that the mayor has _____ the town government by accepting personal favors from local businesspeople.

Group 3

apt	amenity	sentimental	lexicon
renovation	myriad	plight	

1. We must direct our efforts toward relieving the _____ of children living in poverty.
2. It's an old factory that has been under _____ as office space.
3. There are a _____ of possibilities.
4. He has a _____ attachment to his old high school.
5. The hotel has every _____ you could want.

Group 4

augment	conglomerate	anecdote	mingle
cliche	versatile	mundane	

1. He told us all sorts of humorous _____ about his childhood.
2. The story _____ fact and fiction.
3. She is a _____ athlete who participates in many different sports.
4. The money _____ his fortune.
5. They lead a pretty _____ life with little excitement.

Group 5

placebo	insulate	peril	ethnicity
aggravate	solicit	syndicate	

1. People are unaware of the _____ these miners face each day.
2. They're afraid that we might _____ an already bad situation.
3. The center is _____ donations to help victims of the earthquake.
4. We are seeking for a material that is able to _____ against cold.
5. His Aunt Beatrice had been kept alive on sympathy and _____ for thirty years.

Group 6

hype	relic	churn	obstruction
cerebral	rhetorical	melancholy	

1. He is a very _____ jurist who has given much thought to what makes our nation's constitution work.
2. He showed them how to _____ butter.
3. He became quiet and _____ as the hours slowly passed.
4. They found a crude stone ax and other _____ of the Neanderthals.
5. My question was _____. I wasn't really expecting an answer.

Group 7

retrospect	protagonist	deduct	harass
lament	allegiance	navigation	

1. You can _____ up to $500 for money given to charity.
2. She was a leading _____ in the civil rights movement.
3. He owes _____ to them for all the help they have given him.
4. She was constantly _____ by the other students.
5. She _____ over the loss of her best friend.

Group 8

symmetry	dangle	assimilate	emulate
hilarious	parachute	usher	

1. Some people don't like his comedy, but I think he's _____.
2. A nurse _____ us into the hospital room.
3. She sat on the edge of the pool, _____ her feet in the water.
4. Many artists _____ the style of their teachers.
5. Schools were used to _____ the children of immigrants.

Group 9

brink	confide	incompatible	relentless
lavish	prophet	glossy	

1. He _____ that he was very unhappy with his job.
2. a _____ display of flowers
3. The hunter was _____ in pursuit of his prey.
4. He is an economist regarded as a reliable _____ of future developments in global economy.
5. I was at the _____ of death when the rescuers arrived.

Group 10

reckless	contentious	succumb	astound
breathtaking	bolster	zoom	

1. What _____ me is that they never apologized.
2. They will pressure you, and you must try not to _____.
3. After a _____ debate, members of the committee finally voted to approve the funding.
4. She came with me to _____ my confidence.
5. He is a wild and _____ young man.

Answers — P107

Word List 5

Group 1

bristle	guru	vanity	poignant

impede	womb	conceivable

1. Caffeine, the stimulant in coffee, impairs the transport of eggs from the ovaries to the _____, they found.
2. They had not lived in every _____ manner, far from it, but what room would there be for the multitude if each individual tried to exhaust the permutations of existence?
3. Her sarcasm wounded his _____.
4. Moore walked slowly past the tiny kitchen and started up the hallway. He felt the hairs on the back of his neck begin to _____.
5. One shouldn't _____ other's progress.

Group 2

confinement	ludicrous	whim	contrive

shrewd	fraudulent	diagonal

1. Various _____ schemes purporting to be from or associated with the World Health Organization (WHO) have been circulating.
2. I often dance around the house on a _____.
3. In terms of physical location, there was still this _____ in space.
4. Next, move to the _____ section at the back-right side of the diamond.
5. I can _____ without your help.

Group 3

taint	clutter	holistic	disparate

mediation	hindsight	burgeon	

1. When performing _____ flow analysis, the scanner models the flow of data within the system.
2. It's _____ and it's everyone's concern, not just the realm of "artistic" types.
3. Someone shouted, and the _____ lights gathered like sparks of a fire returning to their source.
4. We are all products of our time and we only have _____.
5. When spring is coming, all trees begin to _____.

Group 4

hunch	somber	blunder	detrimental

disdain	ominous	disillusion	

1. But he made an awful _____.
2. This partly reflects a _____ that consumers have more power in an increasingly crowded market for goods.
3. He curled his lips in _____.
4. Lime in the soil is _____ to some plants.
5. There is a whole world of anxiety and _____ behind those bald employment figures.

Group 5

enchant	behold	dismal	perpetual

plump	hue	paranoid	

1. This is my _____ loyalty to my faith.
2. You think I'm _____, but I tell you there is something going on.
3. The changing light patterns will _____ people of all ages.

4. Don't let your lips get dry and scaly _____ them up!
5. The _____ science, it seems, is an optimistic profession.

Group 6

orchestrate	renounce	revere	adamant
pastime	caricature	latent	

1. So in that sense, there is a certain degree of _____ support for him.
2. In support of Western policy, aimed at forcing Hamas to recognize Israel and _____ violence, Egypt has joined with Israel to enforce its blockade on Gaza.
3. Chimps do yawn, and they, like us, respond in kind when shown a computerized avatar indulging in the _____.
4. Rise in the presence of the aged, show respect for the elderly and _____ your God.
5. In truth, Chinese workers were never as docile as the popular _____ suggested.

Group 7

prairie	patronize	traverse	budgetary
forage	inscribe	mural	

1. I'll never _____ that store again.
2. Several railroads _____ the district.
3. About 160 species of rare birds live in the swamps and _____ there.
4. They were forced to _____ for clothing and fuel.
5. For _____ reasons, the redevelopment of these systems from scratch can be a poor option.

Group 8

outburst	thrash	indict	lofty
eminent	oblivious	overdue	

1. The judge ruled that Kennedy "was probably guilty of criminal conduct" but made no move to _____ him.
2. The _____ startled even me and I started laughing to myself.
3. Virtue is _____ but it requires you to give.
4. Then we ask a group of hooligans to go into the rooms and _____ the rooms.
5. No university that I know of is _____ to the revolutions of network and Web.

Group 9

rectify	stigma	involuntary	predicament
wither	triumphant	conspire	

1. Failing some rain soon the crops will _____.
2. Do you ever have _____ leg movements while you are awake?
3. You should _____ your error before it is too late.
4. You _____ with him against me, do you?
5. The next four or eight years may be a disappointment, a _____ renewal or something in between.

Group 10

refurbish	fumble	futile	deflect
impart	clumsy	mutant	

1. The _____ DNA miscoded a single amino acid.
2. One way to _____ all the incoming animosity is by spreading the wealth.
3. However the decisions by Warner Bros to buy and _____ the Leavesden studios in north London may help delay the descent of British cinema into a cottage industry.
4. We do not fight global warming because it is _____ to do so.
5. If Campbell returns to Arsenal, he wants to _____ the knowledge of those past glories to the present squad.

Answers — P108

Word List 6

Group 1

fervor	elongate	dreary	detour
erroneous	savvy	allure	

1. Now, over the past three decades, China has embraced capitalism with the same level of _____.
2. No _____ ideas should be allowed to spread unchecked.
3. The _____ and charm of Paris excite all who visit there.
4. During the _____, the company continued to believe that the marketplace product held promise and decided not to abandon it .
5. I hate these dry _____ days.

Group 2

repercussion	eclectic	subversive	coax
bounty	detract	attire	

1. Whenever a car backfires I have to _____ them out from under the couch.
2. China succeeded in exploding its first atom bomb which provoked great _____ around the globe.
3. This year I'll risk my good-girl reputation with a _____ idea: go bankrupt in 2009.
4. Universities offer an _____ mix of courses.
5. Your interview _____ should match the dress code of the company or be one step up.

Group 3

synchronize	defiant	hysteria	garrison
deport	avid	apprehend	

1. They are giving a _____ answer to the question: You can't do that with glass, can you?
2. She's love to tell Comus something about chastity, but he has neither ear nor soul to _____ the sublime notion and mystery.
3. She praised the government's decision not to _____ the migrants.
4. The film does not _____ with sound.
5. He had become an _____ and accomplished gardener in France.

Group 4

acronym	varnish	legislate	floral
charisma	miraculous	circumvent	

1. The wounded man made a _____ recovery.
2. The first law of regulation is that bureaucrats and lawyers make regulations and bankers and markets learn to _____ them.
3. She engraved the ring in a _____ pattern.
4. The floor is coated with _____.
5. Every woman has her own unique brand of _____.

Group 5

blight	pavilion	remorse	sneer
delinquency	vindicate	epoch	

1. Last but no least, the shortcoming in education is the cause contributing to juvenile _____.
2. How would you _____ your failure to your family?
3. I was uncomfortable with his _____.
4. The _____ of revolution creates great figures.
5. Or would it matter at all since you're already living each day to the fullest with no regrets or _____ as though it could be your last?

Group 6

decency	heady	improvisation	deplore
compulsive	reprimand	cumbersome	

1. The _____ process and cacophony of messages is all about honoring the First Amendment to them.
2. Two colonels received letters of _____ for those failures.
3. Most people with OCD struggle to banish their unwanted thoughts and _____ behaviors.
4. He has no _____, no discipline.
5. She is right to _____ the pogroms against Jews and the beginning of the inquisition.

Group 7

prerogative	aversion	illiterate	impartial
flamboyant	immaculate	captivate	

1. He is an _____ judge.
2. Say no is your _____.
3. I was an _____ in the old society, but now I can read.
4. Still he didn't molest her: for which forbearance she might thank his _____, I suppose.
5. The allure and charm of Paris _____ all who visit there.

Group 8

idiosyncratic	abort	respite	blockbuster
reproach	brag	rendezvous	

1. Do not _____ or bluff.
2. The difference between us and a Hollywood _____ is that we have to keep it tied to the science as closely as possible.
3. Do not _____ yourself; it was not your fault.
4. They decided to _____ the two teams at the club.
5. She could still leave him and _____.

Group 9

tapestry	brook	culinary	liken
complacent	veer	resurgence	

1. Sunlight faded the _____.
2. Are we praising a person or not when we _____ him to a tiger?
3. Don't be _____ over occasional success.
4. I cannot _____ his arrogance.
5. Also the Afghan _____ tradition is very tolerant in replacing meat in pilaf.

Group 10

disclaimer	counterfeit	treacherous	brim
sloppy	accentuate	vernacular	

1. It is a crime to _____ money.
2. Paraphrase the ancient Chinese prose in _____ language.
3. And her _____ sister Judah saw it.
4. Do not roll the _____ as this will highlight the ears.
5. When your clothes look _____, so do you.

Answers — P109

Word List 7

Group 1

clandestine	impeccable	impasse	hallucination
fledgling	crux	barter	

1. This is the _____ of the matter.
2. Their _____ mission: to get you to the fun faster.
3. A deadlock as in negotiations; an _____.
4. We see Christianity, this _____ movement, starting to imitate the structures of the Roman Empire.
5. I added his _____ logic to my stump speech for the rest of the campaign.

Group 2

enumerate	estrange	ambience	translucent
categorical	ferment	dismissive	

1. Although the values are numeric, association rules mining requires the values to be _____.
2. Let me _____ many flaws in your hypothesis.
3. As to her own life those good friends for years gradually _____ since she's always on the run.
4. The execution window can be made _____ so that the application under test can be seen behind it.
5. You might say it with disgust, disbelief or a _____ tone, but you don't scream it.

Group 3

derail	imbue	consummate	fathom
etiquette	legitimize	expiration	

1. This craft would be able to _____ any incoming comets or other outer-space projectiles that might be hurtling towards Earth.
2. It is, in general, hard to _____ what he sees or thinks, which is both the point and a bit of a problem.
3. The restored jade burial suit fully reveals the _____ skill of the laboring people of ancient China.
4. Soon, more than a trillion items will be able to send and receive data about their price, whereabouts, and _____ dates.
5. The point is to enrich your life with people that inspire you, challenge you and _____ life with a richness that can't come from private successes alone.

Group 4

pious	fervent	apathy	phobia
embroidery	palpable	zigzag	

1. Both her father and mother were _____ Christians who regularly conducted home devotions and faithfully attended church.
2. The tension between Amy and Jim is _____.
3. I'm into the _____.
4. That chasm is reflected as well in the widespread _____ of the public toward the election. .
5. Lots of men and women in the West are _____ supporters of bloodstained setups.

Group 5

suffrage	intricacy	aptitude	deflate
idyllic	unscrupulous	rife	

1. In language learning, it is attitude not _____ that determines success.
2. The _____ of the structure may be caused in part by material ejected from a binary central star.
3. An _____ attorney might help you but it will likely be expensive.

4. General elections with universal adult _____ were held in April 1965, with several political parties represented.
5. It operates in a country where fraud is _____.

Group 6

thrift	ameliorate	bloodshed	expedient
quirk	contagious	bribery	

1. He was charged with _____.
2. Should his condition _____ the sentence?
3. This disease is not _____.
4. They accepted her attitude as one of her little _____.
5. Shift your attention from the _____ to the important.

Group 7

emphatic	exuberant	cadence	superfluous
mire	frivolous	archaic	

1. These experts were _____ in their recommendation that health care staff, carers and family contacts of patients be vaccinated against pandemic influenza.
2. Each had his heart rate, power output, pedal _____, enjoyment of the music and feelings of how hard the riding felt monitored throughout each session.
3. Everyone looked fit and well and appeared to be in supremely good health as well as _____ and excited mood.
4. For example, if you're writing a serious story about a natural disaster, the headline should not be _____.
5. And I feel like it's _____ in a way that it's a long list of stuff sorted by date and time or sender, and we waste so much time sorting.

Group 8

aloof	antidote	tantalize	dogma
calibrate	penchant	congest	

1. There is also reason to think that our _____ for making unhealthy choices might be enhanced by the abundance of particular foods.
2. From the Moon Earth is an ideal reference point to _____ the cameras.
3. It has graphics that dazzle your visual sense and sounds that _____ your ears.
4. It is precisely such ignorant people who take Marxism-Leninism as a religious _____.
5. Her hospitality thawed out his _____ manner.

Group 9

recoil	wager	sieve	topography
peddle	callous	defuse	

1. The combination of _____ and weather can be deadly as well.
2. After _____ in horror when she realized it wasn't her boyfriend, she told the man to get out of her room.
3. To me there is something inhuman, something _____ and almost bovine in the practice.
4. His routine work is to rub the coal through a _____.
5. Finally he found his game with whom he stood in to _____ his smuggled watches.

Group 10

bask	backfire	grueling	austere
courteous	egalitarian	vigilant	

1. Even our most carefully laid plans may _____.
2. He comes over as a rather serious, studious and _____ man, but there is clearly another side to him.
3. Yet he went on to win the Tour de France, one of the most _____ sports events.
4. Yes, we're more _____ against those who threaten us, and there are inconveniences that come with our common defense.
5. And then they show them off upon return, both to remember their trip and to let others _____ in their glory.

Word List 8

Group 1

comprehensible	commendable	pelt	conundrum
forestall		ephemeral	cryptic

1. But all kinds of fame are _____.
2. Such initiative is highly _____.
3. Your code should be easily _____, read well and be well documented.
4. Leave _____ messages on the typewriters.
5. These are all international efforts to _____ a financial crisis.

Group 2

reminisce	hinterland	evasive	feign
banal		laborious	bequeath

1. The _____ and obvious truth is that life and a country are largely what you make of them.
2. The driver is believed to have taken _____ action to avoid a girl who stepped out in the road.
3. He spotted a demand from women in China's _____ for branded cosmetics and advice on how to use them.
4. Look at old photographs and _____.
5. Most people _____ their property to their spouses and children.

Group 3

carefree	archetypal	delude	scrawl
vestige		euphemism	deft

1. For the majority of women who have given birth, these "sensations" are a _____ for pain.
2. These are _____ users whose characteristics are distilled from our primary research.
3. There's not a _____ of truth in the humor.
4. Neither side should _____ itself that it

can avoid the harm caused by an increased mutual antagonism.
5. He found a note on his kitchen table. It was a dinner invitation for that very night, in a childish _____.

Group 4

figurative	incongruous	condescend	elate
interminable	amalgamate		laud

1. _____ language is not only a good way to put things into perspective, but metaphors are easier to remember than a complex set of interactions.
2. She was small and fragile and looked _____ in an army uniform.
3. The company has decided to _____ with the parent firm.
4. These people should change this bad habit and _____ to be pleased with what is pleasing, without worrying needlessly about themselves and others.
5. His eye, _____ with happiness, was reading eagerly the tearful gaze of Haidee, when suddenly the door opened.

Group 5

circumscribe	understatement	twine	coalesce
commemoration	partake	quintessential	

1. Additionally, support requires the adoption of one or more policies controlling whether and how to ever _____ small chunks.
2. Better yet, visit the museum beside it and buy your own _____ ball starter kit in the gift shop.
3. The army evidently fears that, under him, its activities would be severely _____.
4. "They're the _____ survivors," he says.
5. It was an honest response and also something of an _____.

Group 6

chide	deride	antipathy	industrious
tact	palatable	demean	

1. Being _____ students, they would write all kinds of notes down.
2. In America, there are voices that _____ and deny the importance of Europe's role in our security and our future.
3. "That is to _____ our humanity because there are always options, always choices, always solutions that human ingenuity can summon," he said.
4. The _____ is mutual.
5. They offer _____ meat, but have not been sought after in the same way as true lobsters or prawns.

Group 7

bigotry	catalyze	unequivocal	annihilate
caustic	incessant	connoisseur	

1. Science is now _____ as to the reality of climate change.
2. She tried to dissociate herself from the _____ in her past.
3. David is something of a sentence _____ and, he says writing a fine sentence is a delicate process—but it's a process that can be learned.
4. The first and far worse type is the End of Life—the crisis that threatens to _____ us by destroying our very existence.
5. _____ rain made conditions almost intolerable.

Group 8

placid	inept	foreshadow	tectonic
pseudonym	introvert	nozzle	

1. He was wandering in the woods one day when quite unexpectedly, he saw a naked maiden bathing in a _____ lake.

2. It struck 80 miles off the east coast where one _____ plate is diving underneath another.
3. Those dark clouds _____ a storm.
4. The filters are comprised of a clay pot set inside a plastic bucket with a _____ at the bottom of it.
5. Historians have even speculated that he was partly-Jewish himself—or even that his mother died at the hands of an _____ Jewish physician.

Group 9

genteel	calamity	purr	juxtapose
pester	sarcasm	onerous	

1. Her _____ wounded his vanity.
2. It was a complete waste of time unless the goal in life was simply to _____ the user for some input.
3. Even a greater natural _____ cannot daunt us.
4. For example, ancient Greek temples _____ tall vertical columns and wide horizontal entablatures to create rigid perpendiculars.
5. She was a good example of a _____ woman, Lydia thought.

Group 10

tumultuous	devious	aloft	commotion
dilapidate	admonish	serenity	

1. Behind all of this _____ are day traders, those creatures of the dot-com era.
2. I have never met someone so _____ in their negotiating tactics as this particular agent.
3. But in the stratosphere they can stay _____ for years, spread by fast winds known as jets, meaning the threat is global.
4. Second, they may indulge in it, thus _____ their study, which isn't rare.
5. Many shrewd billionaires have succeeded in prospering despite the _____ conditions.

Answers — P111

Word List 9

Group 1

equivocal	omniscient	formulaic	irrevocable
extraterrestrial	regal	perturb	

1. NASA has started a 10-year search for _____ intelligence.
2. What _____ me is that magazine articles are so much shorter nowadays.
3. He sat with such _____ dignity.
4. It may be well worth waiting for better times before making any _____ commitment.
5. His paintings are contrived and _____.

Group 2

paucity	abhor	oscillate	succinct
vehement	hubris	indelible	

1. If you have something to say, make sure that it is accurate, _____ and to the point.
2. Man, out of _____, wanted an image formed of himself as a perfected and potentially infinite God.
3. Oil markets _____ on the day's reports from Geneva.
4. It leaves _____ stains on clothes.
5. He was a man who _____ violence and was deeply committed to reconciliation.

Group 3

abridge	colloquial	annul	convoluted
inexhaustible	extrovert	automaton	

1. Then, too, George used a _____ speech, as Sir and Little Miss had not.
2. The _____ Charley Lunn was unlikely to make a quiet exit.
3. She has an _____ supply of enthusiasm.
4. Opposition party leaders are now pressing for the entire election to be _____.
5. Then the Cathedral seemed to pull again on the invisible rope, and I found myself moving down the drive like an _____.

Group 4

unanimity	crevice	sensuous	omnipresent
didactic	transitory	wistful	

1. However, it was Ramses who found the pistol wedged in a _____ in the rock some twenty feet from the tent.
2. He is more _____ in his approach to the learning process.
3. The heat and the steam were relaxing, and I spent a long time in _____ daydreams.
4. Most teenage romances are _____.
5. What makes me feel rather _____ is that there is no one in whom I can confide.

Group 5

vandalize	ceaseless	auspicious	fickle
harbinger	hypnotize	opacity	

1. The walls had been horribly _____ with spray paint.
2. A hypnotherapist will _____ you and will stop you from smoking.
3. Orta's weather can be _____.
4. "I am sure the gods will be kind on such an _____ occasion," said Desmond Featherstone.
5. He insisted that the mineral content of the water determined the _____.

Group 6

irreconcilable	flagrant	governess	fluster
insurmountable	connote	transgress	

1. These old concepts are _____ with modern life.
2. Helen, two years younger, didn't yet go to school, but instead had a _____.
3. She was a very calm person. Nothing could _____ her.
4. The crisis doesn't seem like an _____ problem.
5. The judge called the decision "a _____ violation of international law."

Group 7

egregious	gloat	enmity	demarcation
cajole	rejuvenate	immutable	

1. This is nothing to _____ about.
2. Still, with all that, he never would tell me the origin of the _____ between the two families.
3. He _____ Mr. Dobson to stand for mayor.
4. Shelley was advised that the Italian climate would _____ him.
5. Chemical laws, the way the elements combine and interact, were formulated as complete and _____ truths.

Group 8

serpentine	rover	whirlpool	furtive
sedative	oratory	diminution	

1. An airplane was moving over a world of forests and _____ lakes.
2. The infinite pain that the warrior-poets worshipped was like a _____ that sucked them down into the dark froth of madness and murder.

3. He walked towards the summerhouse, at first _____, then with more confidence.
4. He displayed determination as well as powerful _____.
5. The president has accepted a _____ of the powers he originally wanted.

Group 9

unfathomable	deferential	heretic	salutary
hyperbole	prosaic	acumen	

1. The _____ Jimmy Hornbeck wasn't there to meet her, eager to cater to her every whim.
2. He was considered a _____ and was ridiculed and ostracized for his ideas.
3. His reward to Noriega for saving his regime was swift and _____.
4. It is a _____ to portray him as one of the greatest visionaries in the world.
5. His sharp business _____ meant he quickly rose to the top.

Group 10

abominable	tinge	infinitesimal	circumspect
exorbitant	succulent	observant	

1. The President described the killings as an _____ crime.
2. She didn't notice the _____ patch of damp beneath it on the dark leather.
3. The banks should have been more _____ in their dealings.
4. _____ housing prices have created an acute shortage of affordable housing for the poor.
5. _____ food, especially meat or vegetables, is juicy and good to eat.

Answers → P112

Word List 10

Group 1

detached	cataclysmic	discernible	preeminence
decorous	bizarre	mollify	

1. It was Tuesday evening, three days after the _____ events of the ruby wedding anniversary.
2. The lights in the street were poor, the face dimly _____.
3. No one doubted the _____ of my father in financial matters.
4. _____ behavior is very respectable, calm, and polite.
5. The investigation was undertaken primarily to _____ pressure groups.

Group 2

composed	sulfuric	credulous	fallacious
vicissitude	contented	rancor	

1. Laura was very calm and _____.
2. Others regarded him as _____, interfering and posturing.
3. Their main argument is _____.
4. Whenever he returns to this place he is happy and _____.
5. I asked, frightened not so much by her words as by the _____ in her voice.

Group 3

commodious	plagiarize	disinterested	provident
spellbind	chauvinism	discriminate	

1. The door opened on to the pleasant, _____ room shared by the Armstrongs, an excuse for a small sitting-room led off to the right.
2. The poem employs as its first lines a verse _____ from a billboard.
3. The current sole superpower is far from being a _____ observer.
4. Her _____ measures kept us safe while we waited out the hurricane.
5. He is incapable of _____ between a good idea and a terrible one.

Group 4

effusive	scrawny	delve into	illegitimacy
exhilarating	defile	pensive	

1. He was _____ in his praise for the general.
2. A thin man came riding down the street on a _____ black horse.
3. It was _____ to be on the road again and his spirits rose.
4. He had _____ the sacred name of the Holy Prophet.
5. He looked suddenly somber, _____.

Group 5

close-knit	flippant	ceremonious	draw on
tenable	counterargument	gluttony	

1. Events over the last year have created a _____ community.
2. Part of her was angered by his _____ attitude, which had marked their relationship from the very beginning.
3. A century ago everyday life was much more _____ than in our anything-goes era.

4. The general's imprudent remarks _____ a public rebuke by the secretary of defense.
5. The only way his role can be clarified and his position made _____ again is if there's a public inquiry.

Group 6

facetious	irksome	stealthy	bane
appealing	blindside	enticing	

1. Nothing is more _____ than the sight of people working all day.
2. Slowly and _____, someone was creeping up the stairs.
3. Rain is the _____ of holiday-makers.
4. There was a sense of humor to what he did that I found very _____.
5. He complained about being _____ by the decision.

Group 7

omnipotent	ambivalent	anticlimax	indigent
unswerving	perplexity	antiquated	

1. Doug lived in the shadow of his seemingly _____ father.
2. She remained _____ about her marriage.
3. It was sad that his international career should end in such _____.
4. And they paid so well, well enough that he could take time to apply his considerable talents to _____ clients who couldn't pay.
5. We will never solve all of the _____ of life.

Group 8

alliteration	amount to	acme	expunge
forbear	equanimity	ineffable	

1. His work is considered the _____ of cinematic art.
2. The experience was something he had tried to _____ from his memory.
3. He _____ to mention her name.
4. The Olympic diver always displays remarkable _____ on the platform.
5. Such a day is an _____ mixture of dream and of reality.

Group 9

cling to	edify	imprudent	enterprising
mimicry	lighthearted	empathetic	

1. That family-oriented show tried to _____ the television audience as well as entertain it.
2. The Government of Jamaica considers it _____ to abolish the death penalty.
3. Debra is a very _____ young black business-woman who is involved in a lot of activities.
4. I was amazingly _____ and peaceful.
5. There's another reason nice people take on too much work: they are overly _____.

Group 10

chance on	curmudgeon	antithetical	abase
efficacious	snobbish	adroit	

1. He _____ the solution to his problem.
2. He was _____ with money and was blessed with the extraordinary Spanish gift of prolific, and even inchoate, invention.
3. Taking a cookie break while studying is one of the most _____ ways of rejuvenating the mind that I have ever discovered.
4. He gave us one _____ glance and then disregarded us.
5. He was unwilling to _____ himself by pleading guilty to a crime that he did not commit.

Answers — P113

1 仅仅完成单词认知往往不能转化为分数的提升；因此强烈建议考生重视这份结合语境与单词运用的配套练习。

2 提高级练习与提高级词表同步完成，建议每完成一个 List 的记忆之后就完成相应的练习。

3 每份练习包含 10 组"7 选 5 句子填空"；考生可以先将 7 个单词的中文意思填在单词下方的方框里，再根据上下文，在句子的空格处填入最恰当的单词。

4 所有练习皆配有答案。

Word List 1

Group 1

tease	lever	bump	batch
raid	synthetic	refugee	

1. She left the hospital and moved into an apartment with a fellow _____.
2. Actually he doesn't like to go there because other children often _____ him because of his long hair.
3. They were going to _____ Warsaw the next day.
4. I tried to avoid her, but it was just my luck to _____ into her.
5. Chlorine reacts with the pigments and dyes in your hair, both natural and _____.

Group 2

punch	lounge	supervise	maternal
knot	buzz	theorem	

1. She wants to _____ the cosmetics shop.
2. She tied a pretty _____ at the end of her pigtails.
3. When boxing, do not expect to have the first _____ be a knock out.
4. Roger calls this the mosquito effect: the bug's _____ makes our skin prickle.
5. I have no desire to have a child, no _____ or paternal instinct.

Group 3

verse	dip	flux	denote

Group (cone/tumor/chapel)

cone	tumor	chapel	

1. Then we could go _____ ourselves in any color we wanted.
2. Please turn this piece of prose into _____.
3. All of this _____ and churning creates enormous anxiety.
4. The pressure on the nerve from the _____ may cause hearing loss and imbalance.
5. The flashing lights _____ dangerous roads ahead.

Group 4

caption	rack	pledge	cholesterol
screw	proclaim	splice	

1. A herald will _____ the new king immediately the old one dies.
2. Each level should have exactly one _____ attribute.
3. Put it in your current projects file _____.
4. None will be hit, I _____ my honor.
5. With the hinge cover removed, we now remove the _____ right under the hinge.

Group 5

par	minority	debut	chloride
shrug	clinical	preach	

1. The material in every step of process must be up to _____.
2. That same year he made his Broadway _____, playing a suave radio journalist.
3. Democracy is not about majority rule; it is about _____ rights.

4. When someone asks me this I just _____ and smile.
5. Those who _____ nonviolence as a rule or law tend to be the most violent of all.

Group 6

semantic	slump	antibiotic	token
tray	stride	stumble	

1. I present this gift as a _____ of our appreciation for what you've done for us.
2. I _____ calmly through inky blackness over ground where we've recently spotted packs of coyotes and a stealthy mountain lion.
3. You may not _____ into anything quite that colorful as you write your vacation postcards.
4. If we all recognize that _____ resistance is one of the greatest threats to public health that we face today, we have to do something about this.
5. The OECD expects global trade volumes to _____ by 13% this year.

Group 7

molecular	ion	fleet	lad
strap	tumble	consonant	

1. The _____ is too loose. Tighten it up a bit.
2. Babies _____ when they are learning to walk.
3. This means that I find Professor Simon's apprehension of the structure of organized action _____ with my own experience.
4. They maintain a very powerful _____ in Oriental waters.
5. You do not get this line from _____ hydrogen.

Group 8

nominal	subsidiary	mortality	interface

feast	numerical	auction	

1. They liquored up at the _____.
2. He put his possessions up for _____.
3. Employees of the _____ would have military experience.
4. First, is the increase merely _____, or have real commodity prices also been rising?
5. Deaths in the World Health Organization's _____ database were distributed among 48 mutually exclusive causes.

Group 9

militant	infinity	yell	stall
longitudinal	plea	scramble	

1. More than three million fans are expected to _____ for tickets.
2. Ben is satisfied with that answer and kind of likes the idea that _____ is big enough to be both odd and even.
3. Why do you _____ and scream so much?
4. I conjure you to hear my _____.
5. She was misrepresented in the press as a _____.

Group 10

sanction	slab	mole	dissertation
syndrome	petition	notation	

1. Turn in your _____ next month.
2. A black _____ on her left arm remarks her.
3. The church would not _____ his second marriage.
4. This example uses the rectangle _____ because it has more room for the roles.
5. So the investigators believe that what is aggregating in these families is more than just the full _____ of autism.

Answers — P114

Word List 2

Group 1

muse	inflict	spacious	pedal
compassion	jerk	pinch	

1. The room is _____ and bright.
2. He could not help having _____ for the poor creature.
3. This same effect protects you when you _____ out candles with wet fingers.
4. The damage you _____ on enemies doesn't change even if your HP is running low.
5. I want to be a better writer and maybe my _____ will provide the motivation.

Group 2

casino	rhyme	encompass	beneficiary
subsidize	artery	boycott	

1. Heart disease and _____ disease will raise your risk of heart disease.
2. It is easier to remember a _____ word for word than straight prose, especially if you are illiterate.
3. The party has threatened to _____ the election because it will not be democratic.
4. During his reign, the borders of Prussia expanded to _____ West Prussia and Silesia.
5. A founding principle was that high-savings countries, like Germany and the Netherlands, would not _____ the living standards of the more profligate.

Group 3

viability	savage	lash	envisage

coupon	exempt	preside	

1. They must do the right thing and vote for the Government to rethink its _____ plans.
2. However, its _____ and effectiveness still have to be established.
3. Many people suggest that the government temporarily _____ taxes on online businesses to support their development.
4. For centuries, black people in America suffered the _____ of the whip as slaves and the humiliation of segregation.
5. The new leader is not content merely to _____ over slow decline.

Group 4

weary	bail	blunt	revolt
doom	retention	glide	

1. The knife is _____.
2. Do you think we can _____ down this glacier?
3. He haggled home and felt very _____.
4. So it is not all _____ and gloom, there are positives in the game today.
5. Autocracy caused the people to _____.

Group 5

dazzle	acoustic	ascertain	hitherto
poise	rein	grate	

1. Strong flashes do more than just _____ one's friends—they distort the quality of the picture.
2. It is difficult to _____ a fiery horse.

3. In our case, we have found the true _____ echo beacon.
4. Genetic sampling allows technicians to _____ a fish's birth stream.
5. For perfect _____ and control on the wing, the golden eagle is arguably the most impressive hunter.

Group 6

glitter	swirl	clamp	wholesale
inmate	foil	tug	

1. Morning dew _____ in the sun.
2. He does _____ business, while his brother is engaged in retail business.
3. Behind him _____ smoke and soldiers.
4. NASA is already working on the technologies needed for the asteroid _____.
5. Black paint, _____ and insulation work together to raise the temperature to the boiling point of water.

Group 7

refrain	overturn	verge	outset
tan	crumble	tout	

1. Albania was on the _____ of turning into another Cuba or North Korea.
2. The damaged wall section had begun to _____ completely.
3. Excuse me, Sir, could you kindly _____ from smoking here?
4. Support for this objective must be designed into the system from the _____ of the project.
5. We saw the canoe _____, throwing its passengers into the water.

Group 8

tenure	groove	tremble	smear

flare	rigorous	cram

1. Would you _____, if I touched your lips?
2. Our teacher is so _____ that he seldom lets up on us.
3. Watch a video of the solar _____.
4. _____ some gel on the blister and cover it with a bandage to help it heal.
5. In Wang's office, communist texts _____ the bookshelves.

Group 9

tread	missionary	theology	lieutenant
peg	shiver	dub	

1. She is on to *War and Peace* and Balzac and lists of works on _____.
2. The movie was poorly _____.
3. Your should be in _____ work.
4. A sudden gust of cold wind made me _____.
5. We however continue to _____ your soils until this is over.

Group 10

morale	insulin	cemetery	naval
nuisance	crunch	ramp	

1. They could not destroy our _____.
2. What a _____ that child is!
3. The harbor is an important _____ base.
4. The plane was searched while parked on a _____ at the end of a runway at the Stockholm airport.
5. The Mayor felt the _____ of bones in his jaw, and his eyes filled with tears.

Answers – P115

Word List 3

Group 1

oust	conspicuous	dictatorship	salient

presumption	streamline	squat	

1. Short, _____, massive-skulled, his presence sent out alarm bells of danger.
2. Both pain and pleasure are _____.
3. The same _____ of innocence goes for copyright and privacy.
4. Some wonder whether the objective should be to _____ the colonel.
5. She is a _____ figure.

Group 2

sprinkle	shudder	overhaul	hygiene

lush	snapshot	monarch	

1. The feel of the cold steel made me _____, and I hastily replaced the weapon in my holster.
2. I felt out of place in such _____ surroundings.
3. Whatever you do, do not _____ salt on any railroad tracks.
4. The _____ was ousted by a military coup.
5. _____ has evolved into preventive medicine.

Group 3

yearn	rumble	villain	bandage

disseminate	bog	vocational	

1. All volunteers become empowered to be an expert can _____ information to the public.
2. The _____ requirements for the practitioners in gas industry are discussed, and the current situation of Chinese gas industry is analyzed.
3. Long ago a great mountain began to _____ and shake.
4. There is nothing mysterious about this; in every aspect of life, we _____ for things to be regular and parallel.
5. He is a _____, but he has some virtue.

Group 4

mesh	chuckle	jockey	hurl

Pope	conjure	limp	

1. It was too weak to lift its _____ paws.
2. Are some people just born as geniuses who can somehow _____ up magical solutions to problems that almost seem impossible to overcome?
3. He was the first _____ to visit the White House.
4. I _____ a few more bottles after the first one, then the books after the bottles.
5. Burton gave a kindly _____.

Group 5

repeal	lime	avert	torment

crest	continuum	jargon	

1. There are moves in Congress to _____ or defer the EPA's power to regulate greenhouse gases.
2. He apologized to _____ trouble.

3. On the _____ of the hill, gnarly juniper and cypress trees preside over a separate association of deer, fox, and lichen.
4. Besides, is it just to _____ one man for the crime of another?
5. Do not let the math _____ intimidate you.

Group 6

recess	pervasive	intercourse	lust
assassinate	fiddle	mar	

1. Gaps in health outcomes have multiple causes, but poverty is the most _____ factor.
2. Nobody ever tried to _____ me.
3. And when you explain, be not too explicit, just as you do not expose your inmost thoughts in ordinary _____.
4. A number of problems _____ the smooth running of this event.
5. He emerged from the dark _____ of the garage.

Group 7

ramble	proprietor	yen	slick
rejoice	trot	anthropologist	

1. The _____ is trying to improve the land.
2. There were a few moments when I could have slipped in the water from _____ rocks, but glad it didn't happen.
3. The horse began to _____.
4. This is the best season for a _____ in the suburbs.
5. We are victorious, wherefore let us _____.

Group 8

fixture	mortal	flex	grumble

frantic	sling	fortress	

1. For myself I do not _____, for I am one of the lucky ones.
2. I love it for its choice of relevant subject matter, and for its _____ and unpredictable pace.
3. You face has 9 muscles beneath your skin that you contort, _____, and move.
4. We all cherish our children's future. And we are all _____.
5. Through the vibration, the materials will slip and _____ on the funnel, moving forward.

Group 9

howl	bowel	vomit	exacerbate
picturesque	wink	blush	

1. He began to _____.
2. He sprang up with a _____.
3. And if the new test became routine it would only _____ that problem, he said.
4. The strong wind made me _____.
5. His words raised a _____ on her cheeks.

Group 10

shred	hiss	rugged	arithmetic
bracelet	shear	customary	

1. That school put particular emphasis on _____ and reading.
2. Yes. It looks pretty _____.
3. When a man wants to marry a girl, it's _____ that he buys her a ring and asks her to marry him.
4. Don't throw sensitive information away; _____ it or lock it up.
5. You can _____ a sheep many times, but you can only skin him once.

Answers — P116

54

Word List 4

Group 1

neutron	shriek	wade	wrath
slant	detergent	redress	

1. Her _____ was dulled by the loud crash of thunder.
2. If the water is higher than the bottom of your knees or is moving too quickly for you to _____ through, climb on top of your car and wait for help.
3. She dunked the shirt in some _____.
4. So I sware in my _____. They shall not enter into my rest.
5. You _____ the pen with an angle of 30 degrees on the paper.

Group 2

haze	aura	avail	elude
patriot	covet	relinquish	

1. Practical and time tested, mastering and practicing the following qualities will make it difficult for success to _____ you.
2. The _____ has burnt away.
3. I am afraid my eloquence did not _____ against the facts.
4. What are people who _____ these things saying about themselves?
5. This place has a special _____ all year long, but at autumn it reveals its best.

Group 3

wail	concur	stoop	enclave
humility	eerie	cardinal	

1. My political views _____ with yours.
2. The staccato of the dancer's heels against the floor, and the sharp bursts of clapping punctuate the singer's haunting _____.
3. How could anyone _____ so low?
4. At the beginning of the journey about several kilometers, the scenery was colorful, and there was the field, where the soil is _____.
5. And I found a path of both, I think, _____ and power to walk down.

Group 4

methane	surrogate	downright	dispel
devoid	undue	banish	

1. Once the national government discovered what is going on, they acted decisively and without _____ panic.
2. We hope the images, we picked up for you today, will _____ this myth.
3. Those whose claims look _____ fraudulent should stand down immediately.
4. I also dismissed the idea of a _____ because of the expense.
5. Imagine a country whose inhabitants eat human flesh, wear only pink hats to sleep and _____ children into the forest to raise themselves until adulthood.

Group 5

pitfall	creek	erotic	sabotage
psyche	inverse	tickle	

1. Their apparent eagerness to _____ the talks reveals the dangers that progress poses for them.
2. In 6% of cases an _____ distribution may occur, with rash mostly on the extremities.
3. Too much or too little information is another

common _____, but it involves more art than science to resolve.
4. His exploration of the myth brings insight into the American _____.
5. This might _____, but it feels divine.

Group 6

scarlet	fanatic	rampant	roundabout
bluff	ail	palette	

1. He had very strong, almost _____, familiarity with the JavaScript language.
2. Do not brag or _____.
3. These discrepancies influence what is likely to _____ you.
4. Tie a _____ cape around your neck if you want to impersonate Harry as a Quidditch player.
5. Malaria is still _____ in some swampy regions.

Group 7

rusty	barb	incense	whack
incubate	flutter	resilient	

1. The lock on the door is _____ and won't open.
2. In citizens like these, we see the best of our country—_____ and hopeful, caring and strong.
3. Penguins travel literally the ends of the Earth to protect their infants, facing Antarctic blizzards while they _____ their eggs.
4. They can also flick their abdomens to forcefully _____ another male.
5. It actually tasted and smelled like _____.

Group 8

clad	anthem	whirl	taper
municipality	stout	synonymous	

1. That is why flowers will _____ down so indifferently and elegantly, and smile so peacefully and tranquilly after the wind and rain.
2. She is slender, whereas he is _____.
3. We should _____ off the amount of time given to work.
4. On any given day, behind a plain wooden door, 15 to 20 casually _____ programmers tap away at computers.
5. The concert concluded with the National _____.

Group 9

mumble	antenna	flea	scribble
gorge	illicit	pulp	

1. Keep your _____ up!
2. Your friend is harming someone else or doing something _____.
3. After a while, the sleeping boy would start to _____, as though searching for something.
4. Instead of lunching with my business associates, I would seek out some cheap cafe, order a meager meal and _____ my harmony exercise.
5. A warm afternoon, the second day of spring, but the air in the _____ had become cold and damp.

Group 10

relegate	infiltrate	rupture	sleek
rebuke	metabolic	flurry	

1. The military said they were in an unauthorized area and suspected of trying to _____ that country.
2. In the event of a large _____, the system would vent directly to the atmosphere.
3. When finally she reached home, the whole estate was in a _____ of searching for her.
4. If you say this is the most important, then you _____ the other facts of life to a secondary position.
5. I would neither judge nor _____ them.

Answers — P117

Word List 5

Group 1

counteract	ledger	lunatic	ruffle
ghastly	obligate	saliva	

1. The evening breeze _____ the pond.
2. The drug will _____ the poison.
3. The contract _____ the firm to complete the work in six weeks.
4. Our mouths filled with _____ when we smelled the delicious dinner.
5. Many people cannot stand his _____ behaviors anymore.

Group 2

retaliate	gild	unwind	ebb
fraternity	fresco	uncanny	

1. She has an _____ sense of direction.
2. Paint it with colors and _____ it with gold.
3. She can _____ the thread in three seconds.
4. One of writer's favorite themes is the _____ of mankind.
5. We are waiting for the tide to _____.

Group 3

clot	forfeit	glisten	scorch
paternal	tint	ransom	

1. Large fires _____ vegetation and clog the skies with smoke.
2. Grandmother's hair _____ a shiny silver.

3. If man put his country in danger by helping the enemy, his life and possessions were _____ to the nation.
4. You will bleed uncontrollably if your blood does not _____.
5. You can see how a _____ can change the overall mood and color of an image.

Group 4

rapport	espionage	exasperate	tantrum
ooze	clench	trample	

1. You will build _____ and trust by interacting with employees.
2. It might open them up to future corporate _____ if they publicly acknowledge they've been hacked.
3. Elephants _____ the grass whether they are fighting or in love.
4. To enrage or _____ someone is to write an abusive personal attack.
5. Eric screams and throws things when he is having a _____.

Group 5

monstrous	guild	prick	flair
trifle	grotesque	caterpillar	

1. The fat old man looks _____ in his tight pants.
2. A _____ melon is clearly not fit to eat.
3. Jack is a person with a _____ for making friends quickly.
4. She felt the _____ of the needle.
5. A _____ transforms into a butterfly.

Group 6

amiable	tamper	hearth	ferocious

fixation	protract	conservatory

1. Edward is very _____ and I love him tenderly.
2. The more human beings _____ with the foods I eat, the worse I feel when I eat them.
3. To _____ the suspense, he paused for a considerable period of time before telling us the result of the experiment.
4. They say that our _____ with GDP and growth is threatening an environmental disaster.
5. He kicked the man to death after _____ quarrels.

Group 7

confiscate	dissipate	hive	crackle

infuse	horde	mischief

1. If they don't get any treat, kids might play a trick or _____ on the owners of the house.
2. He confronted their leader and threatened to have the authorities _____ their equipment.
3. The most important member of any _____ is the queen bee.
4. Can you feel the _____ of electricity in the wind?
5. We talked to the _____ of press people who had gathered.

Group 8

hump	corollary	treason	deadlock

bombard	sluggish	elapse

1. The downloads are fast but the _____ web browsing drives me crazy.
2. He was less likely to be merciful when it came to _____.
3. At least four months _____ after it issues a deportation notice.
4. The _____ says that the energy in the universe is conserved.
5. When fresh food and water are not available, the camel can feed off its _____.

Group 9

feud	prelude	throb	throng

promulgate	pedigree	quaint

1. Don't _____ a policy that will destroy social bonds.
2. That horse is from a royal family and has an impressive _____.
3. Insults only served to inflame the _____.
4. Romance is the _____ to a long-term happy marriage.
5. Do we share the same _____ of excitement in our blood?

Group 10

knuckle	superstition	strew	anesthetic

instantaneous	gulp	seclude

1. They serve the wine in little metal cups and _____ rose leaves upon it.
2. Should we sip water or _____ it during a workout?
3. You can have _____ response through internet.
4. His mother helped him clean his fingers to the _____.
5. No one can _____ himself from the outside, or he could not survive.

Answers — P118

Word List 6

Group 1

appease	distraught	porous	doze
margarine	mime	scuttle	

1. The move was widely seen as an attempt to _____ critics of the regime.
2. It's disgusting to see mice _____ across the floor.
3. He is a talented _____ actor.
4. Nina tries to console the _____ Linda.
5. Some students go to bed late at night and often _____ off in class.

Group 2

outstrip	grimace	vulture	nocturnal
panorama	custodian	pamper	

1. I choose to _____ myself when I'm not in a good mood.
2. The supply will keep pace with or _____ demand by the end of this year.
3. The bank needs a _____ of the currency.
4. They attack the dying army like a _____ on prey.
5. Bugs are _____ , so you will be able to trace where they live if you see one wandering at night.

Group 3

dabble	ripe	babble	rummage
conveyance	superimpose	magnification	

1. I _____ around for a pot, a place and a knife in the kitchen.
2. A light fast-sailing ship is mainly used for the _____ of royal goods and important persons.
3. Babies love repetition, which initially encourage them to mimic your voice and _____ sounds and words.
4. We can _____ our logo onto the products of our company.
5. The detector mush enlarges shape as the in-focus image changes shape with _____ .

Group 4

meddle	rehabilitate	tavern	besiege
replenish	inert	exude	

1. They try to _____ the function of that robot.
2. Beckham was drinking alone in the middle of the dark _____ .
3. Bright purple can _____ a magical and elegant feeling.
4. The United States government does not have the right to _____ with other countries' affairs.
5. A military unit continued to _____ the major central city with bombardment and fire.

Group 5

sear	inconceivable	trudge	vista
condone	tingle	squander	

1. We do not _____ or tolerate discrimination within our business for any reason.
2. It sounds _____ but is the naked truth.
3. The dish is thickly dusted with Sichuan pepper and it leaves a _____ on lips and tongue.

4. There are no excused to _____ your time.
5. We have to _____ in the mud and puddles to go back home.

Group 6

supplant	retribution	hoot	cringe
glimmer	overture	sanitation	

1. We have some programs for clean water and _____.
2. In the east there is the slightest _____ of light.
3. You might _____ if you see someone cut their fingers with a knife.
4. The government has made a significant peace _____ by opening the door to negotiation.
5. He didn't want any further involvement for fear of _____.

Group 7

benefactor	wry	uproar	instigate
liquidation	raucous	resound	

1. The company is asked for a _____ of its assets.
2. Matthew allowed himself a _____ smile.
3. The announcement caused _____ in the crowd.
4. The president apologized for the _____ protests.
5. He did not _____ the riot or even know of it beforehand.

Group 8

prefix	sanity	catapult	italic
swerve	righteous	eschew	

1. They should focus on the task and _____ anything that may hinder them.
2. The cost of the item was _____ by a dollar sign.
3. Every time he saw the teacher walking along the road, he would _____ to hit him.
4. He is accused of throwing a petrol bomb and being armed with a _____ during a previous riot.
5. The names and scores of the winning teams are in a bold, _____ font, which makes them really stand out.

Group 9

cyclical	ingest	bosom	serpent
meditate	animosity	vertex	

1. The stock keeps jumping up and reaches no _____.
2. People must _____ at least 500 calories a day.
3. She feels an ache in her _____.
4. The _____ called Eve and gave her an apple.
5. The _____ this actress has stirred up even led to thoughts of suicide.

Group 10

elucidate	buoy	retract	detest
crutch	goggle	exalt	

1. It is unacceptable to _____ what we called a filthy past.
2. The tax breaks should help to _____ the economy.
3. There is no need for him to _____ his ideas.
4. I _____ those who deceive me.
5. I will forgive you only if you _____ your statement.

Answers — P119

Word List 7

Group 1

troupe	compatriot	sterilize	invigorate
gully	boulevard	annotate	

1. She had to keep bringing forth new ideas in her dance to support her chief position in the _____.
2. He fired his knife to _____ it.
3. Liu Xiang's _____ Shi Dongpeng won the second place in this round.
4. We should give a freer rein to small enterprises to _____ them.
5. You can _____ the article to help the students to understand.

Group 2

haggle	speckle	bicker	manicure
truss	impel	gash	

1. She was _____ up with rope.
2. Women love to have _____ as well as spa occasionally.
3. They finished years of _____ by divorcing.
4. The iceberg made a _____ in the hull of the ship.
5. His keen interest in the American Civil War _____ him to make repeated visits to Gettysburg.

Group 3

impenetrable	decry	meltdown	prank
append	courtier	unparalleled	

1. Sir Walter is the famous explorer and _____ of Elizabeth I .
2. Hiding our teacher's bike from her was a great _____. She was looking for it for hours.
3. The Renaissance was an epoch of _____ cultural achievement.
4. In the heat of an economic _____, the struggle for survival can compromise societal niceties.
5. The ancient temple was surrounded by vast stretches of _____ jungle.

Group 4

melodramatic	dew	autocratic	forsake
finesse	consecrate	hash	

1. They planned to _____ the priest in the new church with great ceremony.
2. Chrissie _____ some apples to make an apple pie.
3. Many audiences complained that the plot is a bit too _____.
4. The Great Recession has created a newly frugal consumer willing to _____ the luxury of eating out in order to pay the bills.
5. Moisture in the atmosphere condensed into _____ during the night.

Group 5

rebuff	coffer	resonant	extol
intrepid	collate	recline	

1. All students in the building can hear the _____ tones of the piano.
2. Melody _____ her pictures all together into one timeline.

3. It is an _____ decision to fight against her enemies.
4. His _____ thoroughly disappointed me.
5. My father put all his gold in his _____.

Group 6

sedentary	judicious	embroil	petrify
swipe	methodical	strident	

1. Just choose what to eat, _____ your credit card and in minutes your food is delivered to you.
2. The _____ tone in his voice revealed his anger.
3. Don't _____ me in your quarrel with your girlfriend.
4. Zakaria, who is _____, reasonable, smooth and intelligent, predicts nothing so rash.
5. Beyonce is a slow and _____ worker, and her drawings reflect the extra care she takes.

Group 7

fussy	resolute	crafty	discord
quail	fungal	gobble	

1. It took his _____ girlfriend a long time to pick on one scarf.
2. I hope you all remain _____ in pursuing your dreams.
3. He _____ at the thought of seeing his ex-wife again.
4. There were dangerous beasts in the river that might _____ you up.
5. More than 10,000 trees in England have been destroyed by the _____ disease.

Group 8

stutter	befall	rescind	obedient
hobble	fictitious	impotent	

1. The persons and events portrayed in this production are _____.
2. The aggression of a bully leaves people feeling hurt, angry and _____.
3. The governor does not have the authority to _____ the ruling.
4. The drought was only one of many hardships to _____ the small country.
5. I was so nervous that I spoke with a little _____.

Group 9

attune	regress	cavern	vanguard
hoe	predate	froth	

1. They are the native people who _____ European settlers in America.
2. Tom didn't know how to communicate with others after twenty years live in the _____.
3. In extreme circumstances, people sometimes _____ to the behavior they exhibited in childhood.
4. Students and intellectuals have been in the _____ of revolutionary change in China.
5. The sea _____ over my feet.

Group 10

repent	cursory	hoax	alkaline
contiguous	unruly	droop	

1. This is a special camp where _____ youths are given their last chance to shape up.
2. The liar _____ the art world into believing that the paintings were long-last DaVinci.
3. Three different ethnic groups live _____ to the area.
4. I have nothing to _____ in this relationship.
5. The mistake is so obvious that even a _____ glance can find it.

Answers — P120

Word List 8

Group 1

hoarse	tassel	suction	dainty
frenetic	impregnate	stampede	

1. Their voices were _____, but they began yelling again.
2. The vacuum cleaner has weak _____.
3. Tiny, _____ sandwiches are served with afternoon tea.
4. The thought of loyalty has been _____ to the citizens by their government for centuries.
5. She got hurt and fell down in the _____ near the Bund during the Spring Festival.

Group 2

rapture	decapitate	gregarious	debunk
drowsy	heinous	kindle	

1. Scientists are working very hard to _____ all these rumors.
2. Men are _____ and generally live in groups.
3. The beauty of the sunset filled everybody with _____.
4. The wood was wet and wouldn't _____ easily.
5. They would _____ their enemies and keep them as signs of victory.

Group 3

docile	perspiration	reticent	pacify
confederate	overbear	incipient	

1. Most analysts are more _____ than talkative.
2. A _____ young pony will go wherever it was led.
3. The _____ nations gather together in order to lower international trade barriers.
4. I have an _____ dislike and distrust of that guy, and I only met him this morning.
5. Inspiration and _____ are the ingredients of success.

Group 4

perfunctory	foreclose	indulgent	tendril
loath	excruciate	insoluble	

1. A few _____ of hair framed her face.
2. The parents are so _____ with their child that he can barely live on his own.
3. Diplomats, ever ready to negotiate new measures, are _____ to dwell on the failure of past ones.
4. She gave the list only a _____ glance.
5. Banks can _____ on a home equity loan within 90 days if you miss payments.

Group 5

canny	supple	wharf	insinuate
derange	precipitous	progenitor	

1. Don't let the stress _____ your mind.
2. I often do yoga to keep my body _____ and healthy.
3. There will be no mountain more _____ than this.
4. Words can _____ a person's character.
5. The ship lies alongside the _____.

Group 6

purveyor	inexorable	recluse	mascot
indistinct	innuendo	zealous	

1. The report was based on rumors, speculation, and _____.
2. The fans are _____ in their pursuit of TFBOYS.
3. J. D. Salinger now lives as a total _____ and has not published anything in more than three decades.
4. "Fuwa" is the _____ of the Beijing Olympic Games.
5. Such latent prints are often incomplete and _____ which may not produce unique matches.

Group 7

indiscretion	antithesis	nectar	zest
inhalation	gullible	outpouring	

1. One should not destroy a young man's career just for a single boyish _____.
2. If impurity is associated with death, it makes sense that its _____, holiness, would be associated with life.
3. The book was written with _____, and if possible it should be read with passion as well.
4. Bees get _____ from flowers.
5. The _____ of such air cannot be good for human lungs.

Group 8

hermit	obviate	disingenuous	parch
irradiate	transfix	valiant	

1. Lily is so _____ that no one wants to make friends with her.
2. The four large lamps _____ the hall.
3. Michael is a _____ and never meets new people.
4. It is only with the _____ and gallant spirit of the travelers that it can be passed through.
5. The grass _____ up in summer.

Group 9

sneaky	propulsion	quench	tussle
vanquish	suffuse	frugal	

1. We thoroughly _____ the campfire before we headed to the next destination.
2. You must _____ your fears.
3. Let love _____ your entire heart.
4. How can I let my three years of hard work be stolen by this _____ bastard?
5. Google operations in China have come under pressure amid the company's _____ with the government over censorship rules.

Group 10

ransack	ventilate	introspective	chubby
fetish	orb	terse	

1. She _____ my apartment for money.
2. Out of the countless celestial _____ twirling in space, the planet Earth remains the only one we can call home.
3. For newly-decorated houses, residents should let them _____ for several months before moving in.
4. I couldn't figure out why someone would have a shoe _____.
5. Babies have big foreheads, little nose, _____ cheeks and big eyes.

Answers — P121

Word List 9

Group 1

demure	indefatigable	missive	inscrutable

dimple	incise	detonation	

1. The clay is _____ to create a design.
2. There was a series of _____ around the base of the building, causing it to come crashing down in a short time.
3. Jack is an _____ laborer who can work from sunrise to sunset.
4. There was one little girl, who was _____ and quiet, with beautiful long hair like Alice in Wonderland.
5. Super symmetry is a magic mirror, and everything in what we imagine to be the real world has its ghostly, mysterious _____ mirror image.

Group 2

undulation	reprehensible	molt	hexagonal

offbeat	ratchet	torrid	

1. Your behavior towards the other team was truly _____, so you're being suspended from the next three games.
2. Like other penguins, it undergoes an annual _____, replacing all its feathers in a few weeks.
3. The performance was refreshingly _____.
4. The record revealed that Indian summer monsoon moved forward rapidly, and climate _____ resulted in the change of the solar radiation.
5. My tongue and throat remained _____ for a time following the endoscopy.

Group 3

freewheel	javelin	humdrum	inimical

bisect	kickback	hieroglyphic	

1. The government received an _____ response rather than the anticipated support.
2. You _____ and hit the ball, and you have to be well coordinated.
3. She liked the movie, but I thought it was _____.
4. The city is _____ by the highway.
5. Several company executives were accused of accepting _____.

Group 4

refract	venerate	cosmonaut	fuzz

carnivorous	scoundrel	figment	

1. As we age the lenses of the eyes thicken, and thus _____ light differently.
2. The attack was not just a _____ of my imagination.
3. A _____ stole my wallet in the super-market.
4. She is _____ as a saint.
5. Wolves are _____ animals.

Group 5

doodle	quixotic	entreat	voracious

schism	naivete	unwitting	

1. They had _____ and unrealistic dreams about the future.

2. She _____ in her notebook instead of taking notes.
3. He has a _____ appetite.
4. She began her letter by _____ me to forgive the boorish of her reply.
5. He kept the truth from his _____ friends.

Group 6

pliable	pedantic	morose	encumber
variegate	orangutan	unremitting	

1. It may seem _____ to harp on what looks like mere procedure.
2. He became _____ and withdrawn and would not talk to anyone.
3. She was recognized for her _____ efforts to improve the lives of people in her city.
4. Lack of funding has _____ the project.
5. Because the leather is _____, it's easy to work with.

Group 7

honk	concord	lullaby	resuscitate
swindle	chlorophyll	trite	

1. She hopes to _____ the currently defunct charity organization.
2. The leader would pursue a neutral and balanced policy for the sake of national _____.
3. She sings a quiet _____ that lulls her child to sleep.
4. This view seems almost _____ today, but in the 1960's it was insurgent.
5. A malevolent businessman _____ investors millions of dollars.

Group 8

palatial	jovial	stoic	misconstrue

ebullient	unfurl	disavow	

1. The chairman _____ the press release.
2. His speech is very wonderful and the audiences are all in a _____ mood.
3. Mike is such an _____ guy who is always full of enthusiasm.
4. She _____ my remarks due to lacking of common sense.
5. He spent the last 8 years building this _____ estate in guard-gated Bradbury Estates.

Group 9

premeditate	loll	merriment	rectitude
demagogue	oblong	fortuitous	

1. Your core supporters will teach you how to appreciate the brand in ways you could never _____.
2. Their house was always filled with joy and _____.
3. That politician is just a _____ who preys upon people's fears and prejudices.
4. The occurrence of such things is by no means _____.
5. He was _____ on the sofa in the shadows near the fire.

Group 10

tinkle	extort	decibel	repulse
frolic	listless	unbridle	

1. The heat made everyone tired and _____.
2. He was arrested for _____ bribes.
3. The troops _____ the attack.
4. Cool water _____ in the stone fountains.
5. A group of Australian sea lions relax and _____ in a sea grass meadow near Little Hopkins Island South Australia.

Answers — P122

Word List 10

Group 1

camphor	entrain	vacillate	demoralization
satiate	otherness	fatalistic	

1. As an American growing up in Africa, I always felt a sense of _____.
2. It was almost as if it were a living organism looking for another victim to _____ its evil appetite.
3. Recently, Jake has been feeling inadequate, and this _____ has had a damaging effect on his work performance.
4. Many people have developed pessimistic _____ opinions about the war.
5. For the next uneasy twelve months, Hillary, now twenty-six, would _____ about whether to marry Bill.

Group 2

facade	hat trick	outsmart	pileup
garrulous	bashful	beguile	

1. She was cunning enough to _____ her classmates into doing the work for her.
2. A _____ of e-mail messages needed to be dealt with.
3. A _____ child hid in his room whenever there were visitors in the house.
4. He became more _____ after drinking a couple of beers.
5. He _____ his enemies.

Group 3

misanthrope	enunciate	don	loquacious

recommence	limber	propellant	

1. It is said that the ship would travel to another port, from which search operations had to _____.
2. Mr. Simpson, normally _____ and chatty, had little to say.
3. He shaped the basket out of _____ branches that could bend easily around a frame.
4. He set out to _____ the basic principles of his system.
5. The young people thought him a gloomy _____, because he never joined in their sports.

Group 4

verbose	avocation	clipping	faddish
fungi	dissolve	flume	

1. She's always interested in the latest _____ items.
2. He is a _____ and loquacious speaker.
3. He breeds dogs as an _____.
4. But without _____ we would not have gardens or forests at all.
5. His kind words _____ her sadness.

Group 5

relict	actuate	denunciate	abash
dissolute	reprove	insuperable	

1. The teacher _____ the student for being late.
2. The building project ran into _____

67

financial difficulties and had to be scrapped.

3. The divide between the civilized, virtuous West and the tyrannical, _____ East began in part with Rome and its Egyptian problem.
4. Nothing _____ him, nor was he appalled by the display and culture around him.
5. People around the world begin to _____ this brutal violence.

Group 6

torpid	equilateral	aurora	cut back
counterclockwise	raconteur	creeping	

1. My tongue and throat remained _____ for a time following the endoscopy.
2. The light creates the _____ that we see.
3. Jack is a well-known _____ who is very good at telling stories.
4. We need to _____ the bushes a bit so that the house number is visible from the street.
5. At this _____ pace of progress we'll never have the float ready for the parade.

Group 7

countermand	fecund	munificent	breeding
extemporize	onomatopoeia	blow over	

1. A _____ host presided over many charitable events at his mansion.
2. Orders to blow up the bridge were _____.
3. At the same time, Asia's rapid urbanization has gobbled up _____ farmland.
4. A good talk show host has to be able to _____ the interviews when things don't go as planned.
5. If you ignore it, the dispute will _____ soon.

Group 8

irretrievable	quitter	importunity	inchoate

recapitulation	parabola	enervate

1. Don't be a _____. I know you can do it.
2. The opposition is _____, its leadership unknown, its aims so far vague and various.
3. The data was _____ after the computer crashed.
4. The surgery really _____ me for weeks afterwards.
5. His _____ left me no alternative but to agree.

Group 9

deject	malevolence	satiric	lionize
filial	debark	glowing	

1. She was _____ everywhere after her novel won the Pulitzer Prize.
2. This is a _____ story about the movie business.
3. Koreans have long regarded _____ piety as the essence of all virtues.
4. Nothing _____ a TV pundit more than the reality check that nobody cares what he thinks.
5. The path ends at the village pub, its windows _____ in the summer twilight.

Group 10

halcyon	ennui	insolence	correctitude
effervescent	cupidity	irresolute	

1. Don't judge him by his arrogant airs, his lordly pretensions or his social liberal _____.
2. Her performance style is _____, entertaining, enthusiastic, and exciting.
3. The company's potential for growth seemed unlimited during those early _____ years.
4. The evidence revealed the _____ of the company's directors.
5. The committee was timid, mediocre and _____.

Answers — P123

全能级 Level 4

1 仅仅完成单词认知往往不能转化为分数的提升，因此强烈建议考生重视这份结合语境与单词运用的配套练习。

2 全能级练习与全能级词表同步完成，建议每完成一个 List 的记忆之后就完成相应练习。

3 每份练习包含 10 组 "7 选 5 句子填空"；考生可以先将 7 个单词的中文意思填在单词下方的方框里，再根据上下文，在句子的空格处填入最恰当的单词。

4 所有练习皆配有答案。

Word List 1

Group 1

hood	mast	pod	sanctuary
brass	scrub	backlash	

1. We _____ and _____ until the floor was clean.
2. She was dressed in a dark cloak, with the _____ pulled over her head.
3. Stainless steel, _____, and other metals also are options.
4. To his relief, he saw temple guardians standing outside the massive doors of the _____.
5. Politicians will face a severe public _____ if power shortages occur.

Group 2

genus	sewer	gospel	tonic
glucose	depot	hinge	

1. An infrastructure of _____ and clean water was vital.
2. The future of the industry could _____ on the outcome of next month's election.
3. We have lots of food in our _____ and we are not concerned about possible shortages.
4. However, we can't always buy every answer as the _____ truth.
5. The crime novel, written from the criminal's perspective, is sometimes seen as a particular species of the detective story _____.

Group 3

mantle	plank	brow	cardiac
snatch	bunk	brood	

1. One family had raised a _____ of chicks in mid-July, and they had already grown quite a

bit by this time.
2. He turned around, pushing his dark brown hair off his forehead and wiped his sweaty _____.
3. They caught up with him, dragged him, _____ the money box and started beating him up.
4. It had snowed for the last few days, and the woods were buried in a perfect untouched _____ of thick fresh snow.
5. Two days after the _____ injury, the hearts of all the rats were removed and examined.

Group 4

mistress	asthma	cane	wardrobe
duct	slit	flute	

1. Bamboos and other _____ often have edible seeds.
2. That gorgeous suit looked like it cost more than my entire _____ combined.
3. The doctor conceded that during his 16 years of occupancy, the air _____ of the building have not been cleaned.
4. Both victims had been stabbed and severely beaten—their throats _____ from ear to ear.
5. Double congrats to the _____ of ceremonies for putting on such a great show.

Group 5

crouch	calf	amplitude	squash
pastoral	foliage	vaccination	

1. She _____ down, and wrapped her arms around her frail body, covering her face with her hands.
2. He stepped on the cigarette, _____ it into the ground.
3. Doctors at the meeting expressed concerns over a lack of available _____ should an outbreak occur.
4. Environmental degradation associated with agricultural and _____ practices has compounded the rural crisis.

5. What is missing is a certain largeness of mind, an _____ of style, the mantle of a calling, a sense of historical dignity.

Group 6

dilute	bulge	boulder	atrocity
outrageous	lineage	tenor	

1. In many cases, these compromises _____ the impact of the proposed reform, often postponing major changes until a later date.
2. Wars often unleash a level of _____ that would be unimaginable in peacetime.
3. My eyes _____ and I stared at the board in bewilderment.
4. The things politicians say and do to either grab for power or remain in office are often _____, sometimes unbelievable.
5. Dad felt that my aristocratic heritage and working-class _____ would make me an ideal political candidate.

Group 7

buckle	stringent	repertoire	trumpet
trajectory	cricket	potassium	

1. Some politicians _____ these results very loudly as some sort of achievement.
2. A guided missile corrects its _____ as it flies, homing in on the heat of a jet plane's exhaust.
3. Collaborations between dance and musical companies broaden audiences and enrich _____.
4. She _____ her seat belt and opened the window to look out on Newark at night.
5. California's air pollution guidelines are _____.

Group 8

pundit	emanate	sewage	beard
ballad	viral	rave	

1. There is no guaranteed way of preventing _____ and bacterial infections.
2. After the game the vast majority of experts and _____ were gushing in their praise of the official.
3. Frankenstein lapsed into a delirious fever for several months, ranting and _____ about killing the monster.
4. There was a gentle warmth _____ from him, and she wanted to be a part of it for a while.
5. This massive influx of new settlers brought with them many of their own traditions, stories and _____.

Group 9

den	psychic	covenant	lest
poultry	brace	hurdle	

1. With a strong determination, she _____ herself and headed out of the dim alley and into the morning sun.
2. One _____ to overcome would regard who actually owned the ground.
3. The marriage _____ is the foundation of the family.
4. She tiptoed _____ the guard should hear her.
5. The building was old and derelict, a suitable place for a _____ of thieves.

Group 10

cohort	butcher	mourn	smack
heave	seam	pastry	

1. Parents will now be the only people legally allowed to _____ children, and childcare organizations say they hope the law will eventually be extended to parents as well.
2. At the policeman's funeral, the mayor of his village _____ him and is sad at the prospect of new burials.
3. The sheets are nailed together at the _____.
4. How to understand the older generation which supported Hitler and his _____?
5. She _____ the sofa back into place.

Answers — P124

Word List 2

Group 1

lurch	boar	berth	mince
syrup	conscientious	lavatory	

1. The potatoes are _____ and mixed with chocolate.
2. Operators must be vigilant, _____ and dedicated in their duties of administering backups and verifying their successful completion.
3. She held on tightly to the side of her seat as the carriage _____ into movement.
4. In Britain, the correct upper class term for toilet is _____.
5. We slept over in the cabin and I was given an upper _____ in one of the rooms.

Group 2

anthology	mink	sympathize	straddle
perverse	jumble	annex	

1. Publishers, agents and editors are always talking about how short story collections and _____ don't sell very well.
2. Not only do we accept them, but we _____ with their actions because we identify with aspects of their personalities.
3. He turned the chair around and _____ it.
4. The refusal by the government to accept the best science is irrational and _____.
5. His desk is a chaotic _____ of books, journals, miscellaneous documents, and baby pictures of his three children.

Group 3

crank	canvass	murky	carp
expatriate	torso	retina	

1. Almost all of my _____ and lower body had been numb in the first place, so the result was merely a dull ache.
2. The truth is that an American _____ has a foreign income exclusion.
3. The sun still shone but somehow it seemed _____ and dulled.
4. He _____ the engine on and sped away from my house.
5. Older adults living with young voters who were _____ also voted at significantly higher rates.

Group 4

countenance	wean	gale	specter
bearer	henceforth	juggle	

1. The doctor tried to _____ her off the sleeping pills.
2. The hereditary banner _____ would carry the Lyon Standard and the Saltire.
3. Racist behavior is criminal, and cannot be _____.
4. According to the new decision, visitors to patients would _____ be required to carry passes.
5. In China, a huge surplus and high savings are raising the _____ of inflation.

Group 5

clasp	snarl	gallop	rue
fallout	tweak	derelict	

1. The blond man stared down at the bottle _____ gently between his hands.
2. She expressed admiration for his work, but _____ her inability to understand his mathematics.
3. The wolves of the group suddenly rushed towards the direction of the sound, baring their teeth and _____.
4. Knights ride their horses at full _____ and are almost all successful at driving a spear

through a 3-inch ring.
5. Following a few weeks of begging on the streets and sleeping in _____ buildings, he falls in with a friendly group of squatters.

Group 6

snort	persecution	latch	retort
baptism	sag	twitch	

1. I walked over to the large oak door and lifted the _____.
2. Cora bit her lip as she forced herself to not _____ to his last remark.
3. Violence, war, poverty, unemployment, crime or _____ drive many others to escape.
4. Her shoulders dropped three inches as she _____ against the doorway, shaking her head and laughing a little.
5. People want priests to competently carry out funerals, weddings, and _____.

Group 7

flounder	erratic	grove	cork
simmer	maiden	intestinal	

1. Reduce heat immediately to keep the water _____, but not boiling.
2. He pulled the _____ from the bottle and poured a glass for each.
3. A witness said Davis, a good swimmer, began _____ in the water.
4. Global warming is also implicated in increasingly _____ arctic weather patterns.
5. One by one the _____ waltzed with the young prince, hoping to win his heart.

Group 8

yank	ledge	creak	graft
chlorine	grope	mash	

1. Not only do the very poor have little or no monetary income, the wealthy are often able to avoid income taxes thanks to corruption and _____.
2. Reacting on instinct, I pulled at his arm, and _____ him back into position.
3. I reach down to the floor and _____ around for my phone.
4. They require a combination of rocky _____ or canyons and open, shrubby areas.
5. _____ avocado is also ideal for babies, since it is mild and creamy in flavor yet higher in vitamins.

Group 9

spectral	toil	ordain	cod
parity	assay	apron	

1. They _____ long hours in appalling conditions in machine shops and restaurants.
2. A laser is the generator of intense coherent, electromagnetic radiation in the _____ range between ultra violet and infrared wavelengths.
3. The striking workers want pay _____ with their counterparts in the public transportation system.
4. In 1803, he was _____ minister of the Federal Street Church (now the Arlington Street Church) in Boston.
5. The cells were cloned and _____ for enzyme activity.

Group 10

macho	ravage	ordinance	barley
ranger	crate	dough	

1. I'm not one of those _____ guys who think men can't cry.
2. After the British evacuated, patriots returned to ruined properties and a city _____ by fires.
3. Park _____ regularly patrol the area and in the summer months they cover it up to 10 pm.
4. Illegal disposal of solid waste is a violation of a city _____.
5. They packed their bags with their clothes and _____ their armor and weapons for transport in the ships cargo bay.

Answers — P125

Word List 3

Group 1

dislodge	birch	obnoxious	puddle
wobble	extrapolate	budge	

1. The smell of cigarettes can be rather _____, even in the street.
2. Scientists attempt to _____ likely human cancers from laboratory studies.
3. The table _____ where the leg is too short.
4. He kicked at the stone to _____ it.
5. I tried to persuade him, but he didn't _____.

Group 2

belie	mercenary	primordial	lug
exponent	beset	resin	

1. She married him for purely _____ reasons because she was a single mother with no means of support.
2. Life seems to have originated in the _____ oceans that covered the Earth four billion years ago.
3. Everyone hopes that the next president will be able to gradually resolve the problems _____ our country.
4. A champion of the poor and an ardent _____ of Christian unity, the Pope was a beacon of light.
5. The brilliance of the sun _____ the low temperature.

Group 3

genotype	antioxidant	sonnet	camcorder
seismic	onslaught	brawl	

1. Early yesterday morning, he was arrested after _____ with two guests at a Brooklyn hotel.
2. Cultural and civil liberty activists ought to unite and fight to resist these _____ on basic fundamental freedom.
3. These lines are in fact the final couplets from five _____ in Shakespeare's poems.
4. Fruits and vegetables are the major food sources of _____ that may protect the lung from oxidative stress.
5. The region experiences a high rate of _____ activity, making it susceptible to earthquake damage.

Group 4

evict	squirt	cub	astute
sizzle	spurious	cadre	

1. In the last general election, no one, not even the most _____ of pundits, foresaw his demise.
2. Landlords will retain the power to _____ tenants who display anti-social behavior.
3. An octopus has no backbone and will _____ ink indiscriminately if threatened.
4. The government has an obligation to act against _____ or fraudulent claims.
5. He trained _____ of engineers and built health clinics and schools in Iraq.

Group 5

glint	plethora	squint	metaphorical
cleave	reprieve	concoct	

1. Her glasses were _____ in the firelight.
2. Salt's ability to preserve and sustain life has made it a _____ symbol in every religion.
3. The ax _____ the rest of the sword in two, missing Drew's flesh by inches.
4. They _____ a preposterous but entertaining story.
5. He was also a multi-talented musician who could adapt himself to a _____ of instruments.

Group 6

anarchist	quip	kiln	condo
circumference	lore	repertory	

1. At home he had been funny, sociable, always ready for a _____ or a practical joke.
2. Romanians have a variety of traditions and _____ dating back to antiquity.
3. At its simplest, pi is the ratio of the _____ of a circle to its diameter.
4. Like libertarians, _____ believe that morality is a matter of opinion or personal taste.
5. The couple was the first to purchase one of 15 _____ in the buildings that date back to the late 1700s.

Group 7

parable	swagger	smirk	protrude
transpire	sumptuous	treadmill	

1. The enemy soldier fell to the ground with the arrow _____ from his back.
2. He _____ as he walked towards her, then sat down on the bench.
3. As the verdicts were read by the jury foreman, some of the defendants smiled, _____ and even giggled.
4. Details about what _____ at the meeting were not released.
5. Their rich, _____ food contrasted with the simple and plain food prepared by the ordinary people of Nepal.

Group 8

quartz	shack	crayon	beige
adrenaline	nascent	crib	

1. My necklaces are made mainly of semiprecious stones, such as agate, _____, amber, rock crystal and jade.

2. The art teacher came up to the lounge with a huge box of colored pencils, markers, _____ and oil pastels.
3. In tents, _____, log cabins and frame dwellings, pioneers gathered together for protection.
4. And there are signs of _____ political and economic reforms, albeit small, tentative ones.
5. The theme in the house seemed to be of neutral and warm shades like tan, stone brown and _____.

Group 9

magnesium	balk	flask	admiral
ford	limelight	stalwart	

1. Fashion has turned the clock back to the Eighties, bringing gold, sequins and bold patterns back into the _____.
2. He looks at the cup, smiles, and adds a little liquid from a _____.
3. Gravely was the first Black to become an _____ and command a major naval fleet in the 1960s.
4. He remained a _____ supporter of the cause.
5. Parents concerned about allergies may _____ at the idea of keeping pets around children.

Group 10

plod	filament	buttress	stash
misdemeanor	meander	abstain	

1. She turned around slowly on her heel and _____ back up the hill.
2. The mother had always been the _____ of our family in trying times.
3. In places the road will _____ and curve to draw attention to the landscape.
4. In earlier ages, Christians sought to purify themselves by _____ from enjoyment.
5. Their wealth had been _____ away in Swiss banks.

Answers — P126

Word List 4

Group 1

conifer	falcon	daffodil	quack

clover	insular	soggy	

1. Unlike most hawks, _____ do not build nests (though caracaras do).
2. Heavy rains over East London the past two weeks have left the outfield _____ and conditions were soft underfoot.
3. Even in famously _____ Japan, travel is producing a far more worldly generation.
4. As for _____, why not leave this attractive plant and good luck charm alone?
5. Evergreen trees, including many _____, support more leaf area than deciduous trees in the same environment.

Group 2

accolade	laurel	deluge	chasm

phosphorus	headlong	blare	

1. Preliminary data suggest this rainfall triggered a 500-year flood _____.
2. Though the building received _____ from the architecture community, many critics considered it inhospitable to the display of art.
3. He fell _____ into the tent.
4. All of a sudden, alarms _____ out over the loud speakers as the facility went on high alert.
5. The _____ between the wealthy elite and broad layers of the population will only continue to widen under conditions of slump.

Group 3

placate	sundry	beget	airlift

commensurate	cobalt	windshield	

1. Jim parked the truck and glanced out through the _____ at the front of the building.
2. Using this vital supply route significantly reduces _____ and sealift costs.
3. Such heavy responsibility must receive _____ reward.
4. She eventually storms off into another part of the house and he follows in an attempt to _____ her.
5. It has been a case of policy errors _____ more dangerous mistakes.

Group 4

coyote	counterpoint	omen	homestead

genial	quibble	exhort	

1. We had a _____ and helpful waiter who led us capably through the menu.
2. In spite of these _____, Lancaster's book should prove a valuable resource.
3. I have used my interviews with parents as a _____ to a professional judgment.
4. A rise in imports might be an _____ of recovery.
5. Moral consequentialism _____ us to choose between different modes of life as well as different choices within each mode.

Group 5

brash	munch	pacifist	garb

muffin	fender	sonata	

1. The program for the evening comprises four of the ten _____ Beethoven composed for piano and violin.
2. At the other extreme were the _____ who rejected any form of violence, even in self-defense.
3. Lily made herself a sandwich for dinner and _____ the remaining slice of bread.
4. We'll be dressed in medieval _____.
5. Being confident does not mean being _____

and aggressive; it means being politely assertive.

Group 6

giddy	bravado	pander	insidious

divulge	precocious	divinity	

1. Quite the reverse, his _____ hides his basic insecurities.
2. Most people with this _____ disease have no idea that they are infected.
3. The Government should not be _____ to public taste in the arts, but rather driving it.
4. As a boy, Freud was intellectually _____ and an extremely hard worker.
5. We tried to make him _____ the name of the winner, but he wouldn't budge.

Group 7

trepidation	pantry	proverbial	apocalyptic

camaraderie	flout	eavesdrop	

1. She opened the window just enough to _____ on the conversation outside.
2. They eat fugu without much fear or _____ because of the confidence they have in licensed chefs.
3. Civil disobedience didn't mean _____ all law.
4. Nuclear weapons can lead to the _____ destruction of the world.
5. Our _____ and patriotic attitude did not evaporate along with the smoke.

Group 8

scourge	wilt	preposterous	squid

sordid	lurid	preponderance	

1. This conclusion is supported by the great _____ of informed commentary.
2. This story is _____ and shameful, and everyone who was involved in producing it should be ashamed of themselves.
3. So _____ seemed the suggestion, a stifled laugh was as much as I could offer by way of a response.
4. In the heat, the grass grows rapidly but the flowers _____ fast.
5. One of the greatest _____ afflicting indigenous peoples in Canada is given only token attention.

Group 9

flint	cation	vagary	wavy

decimate	blurt	infidelity	

1. She wouldn't _____ out words she did not mean.
2. Her _____ brown hair was messy, tangled, and pulled into a sloppy ponytail at the nape of her neck.
3. She was convinced that her husband was guilty of _____.
4. Populations of these invertebrates have been _____ or even eradicated in areas where wasps are common.
5. They withstood the _____ of nature and remained mute witnesses to the changing times.

Group 10

primal	whimper	quash	recalcitrant

nimble	noxious	spurn	

1. Residents' associations should be authorized to fine _____ drivers who do not turn up at fixed timings.
2. She was accused of being superior and distant—because she _____ requests to appear on television or model for magazine covers.
3. The court of appeal may dismiss the appeal, _____ the judgment, or request a retrial by a trial court.
4. The origin of these summer traditions is a _____ herd instinct, the urge to join with others in a festive act.
5. The courts have experienced problems over the definition of poison or other _____ thing.

Answers — P127

Word List 5

Group 1

enviable	mafia	meek	apparition
motley	epiphany	recrimination	

1. A _____ crew of tourists filled the beach.
2. My little sister is as _____ as a lamb when she was a kid.
3. This is not a time for _____, but a time to come together in solidarity.
4. Clair has the _____ advantage of experience among the three candidates.
5. All the restaurants in Chinatown are under the _____ control.

Group 2

forlorn	cardiology	stocky	extricate
mottle	beaker	microcosm	

1. Berlin is in _____ of Germany.
2. He was trying to _____ himself from official duties.
3. He sounded _____ in the phone after the breakup.
4. The cow's coat was light red _____ with white.
5. Although short, he is _____ with great physical strength.

Group 3

demur	emulsion	profane	phonograph
lilac	crescendo	astride	

1. With the advent of _____ recordings, her music was able to be preserved.
2. The painting portrays him sitting _____ on a horse.
3. Steve accepted the proposal without _____.
4. He is a _____ man with no respect to our sacred temples.
5. Surprisingly, the reluctant cheers began to _____.

Group 4

ode	polygon	ethereal	apportion
clang	stratify	viscous	

1. Pentagon is a kind of _____.
2. Voting power will be _____ according to contribution.
3. The iron gate _____ shut behind him.
4. Her _____ beauty seems too perfect for this world.
5. Most developed countries are _____ societies.

Group 5

sequester	knead	acquiesce	bouncer
concentric	extraneous	dictum	

1. She did not take those _____ considerations into account.
2. His loss struck him so hard that he _____ himself from the rest of the world.
3. Sara _____ in his decision.
4. Aunt Susie taught her to make butter, to _____ bread, to make jam.
5. The _____ prevented that motley of students from entering the pub.

Group 6

accretion	shard	anachronistic	ostrich
fizzle	arrowhead	infatuation	

1. The firework _____ and went out.
2. His crush for the girl developed into an _____.
3. That _____ of glass in her heel hurt her so bad that she can't stand straight.
4. It was the _____ of small victories from local government that ultimately transformed into national victory.
5. She is rebelling against the _____ morality of her grandparents.

Group 7

penance	reincarnation	pail	coy
paltry	forebear	deleterious	

1. Divorce is assumed to have _____ effects on children.
2. He is said to be a _____ of the Hindu god Vishnu.
3. She would earn a _____ $33 more each month.
4. He had done public _____ for those hasty words.
5. She is _____ about her age.

Group 8

vale	perforate	wiry	replete
conveyor	suture	mauve	

1. A shell fragment _____ his left lung.
2. A _____ of goods is running on the road.
3. She seems a _____ girl standing next to the stocky boy.
4. The textbook is _____ with facts, figures and charts.

5. It bears clusters of _____ flowers in early summer.

Group 9

sentinel	induct	blasphemy	loiter
eulogy	tundra	hew	

1. A wide course had been roped off and _____ with police.
2. Some artists took photographs that _____ to a more traditional idea of art.
3. They were _____ along the river bank, talking and laughing.
4. The new governor was _____ into his office.
5. It is _____ to say that the temple is ugly.

Group 10

metamorphosis	atrophy	malleable	clank
lodger	decadent	mannerism	

1. Excessive TV viewing may lead to _____ of children's imaginations.
2. That _____ is a sweetheart, cleaning up and helping out all the time.
3. Anna has been persuaded enough to be _____.
4. His _____ from an athlete to an entertainer is surprising.
5. He grew up by learning great men's speeches and studying their _____.

Answers —— P128

Word List 6

Group 1

fractious	squalid	separatism	vivacious
obstinate	regent	overshoot	

1. She never fought like _____ child.
2. It is unusual for two such _____ people to have a happy marriage.
3. He had _____ by fifty yards but quickly returned to the finish line.
4. That is a _____ attempt to save themselves from electoral embarrassment.
5. Sadly, their _____ boy had become moody and morose.

Group 2

germane	redolent	platitude	mongrel
bulldoze	heft	detritus	

1. Her _____ about how exercise makes us healthy is boring.
2. His family name suggests _____ of history and tradition.
3. The whole city is littered with military _____.
4. That inquiry is not _____ to our theme.
5. Doug helped us _____ the kegs up into the truck.

Group 3

retroactive	joystick	encrust	cellist
rascal	lactose	narcissism	

1. The _____ from that orchestra is lovely.

2. That big _____ tax increase hindered the development of the economy.
3. the dried and _____ blood on the scar itches
4. The main character is a stupid _____.
5. He is deeply indulged to _____ that he cannot see his own defect.

Group 4

gaiety	bohemian	fructose	ravish
explicate	thrall	inferno	

1. The _____ writer used some unconventional elements in his new book.
2. She attempts to _____ the relationship between justice and freedom.
3. He seemed to be a part of the _____, having a wonderful time.
4. She was in _____ to her abusive husband.
5. _____ by the beautiful music, she feels like that she fall in love with the cellist.

Group 5

pejorative	commandeer	metamorphose	brusque
chasten	honeycomb	languid	

1. The terrace was perfect for boring _____ days in the Italian sun.
2. She is _____ and impatient during the fight.
3. The director was somewhat _____ by his recent flops.
4. Telegraph and telephone lines were _____ by the generals.
5. His remarks were considered too _____ for the daytime radio.

Group 6

ruse	cogent	interlace	diatribe
capsize	berserk	harangue	

1. Eleanor tried to think of a _____ to get Paul out of the house.
2. After she left him, he went _____, throwing things about the apartment
3. Her _____ argument convinced even the most obstinate man.
4. Hurt by the _____, she decided not to direct any more.
5. He is the kind of guy who would _____ total strangers about PCB levels in whitefish.

Group 7

mandible	inculcate	slosh	canary
snobbery	contort	paragon	

1. Your cook is a _____ from which I should learn.
2. They will try to _____ you with a respect for culture.
3. Her face _____ with anger.
4. His parents have a reputation for _____, having respect only for those in the upper class.
5. The _____ in the cage has a bright yellow plumage.

Group 8

tepid	subjugate	tirade	husk
concierge	vilify	horticultural	

1. The hotel _____ gave us a map of the Central Park.
2. The Normans had _____ most of the Ireland's population.
3. The audience gave a _____ response to her harangue.
4. She gave a long _____ of abuse to the newly published book.
5. He has been _____ in the press about her new movie.

Group 9

abysmal	gradation	lopsided	delectable
ramshackle	sawdust	locomotion	

1. The _____ competition is unfair.
2. Within the carpenter family, there is a _____ according to carpentry ability.
3. The quality of the music is _____ and it hurts by ears.
4. The _____ Ms. Davis soon made a lot of friends after she moved to the new neighborhood.
5. She lives in a poor _____ cottage.

Group 10

gaffe	curd	throwback	ascetic
culpable	imp	countervail	

1. Calling the voters "deplorable" is a serious public _____.
2. He is a cheeky young _____ who likes jokes.
3. I hold you _____ for the damage your team has done.
4. He lives an _____ life in which no entertainment is allowed.
5. The advantage of the party was mediated by a number of _____ factors.

Answers — P129

Word List 7

Group 1

peremptory	virulence	intermission	genie
laconic	diehard	charlatan	

1. His _____ reply suggested a lack of interest in the topic.
2. The daily work goes on without _____.
3. "Just do it!" came the _____ reply.
4. That speech is a _____ attack on liberalism.
5. She was a _____ Yankees fan.

Group 2

logbook	domineer	vagabond	jowl
astrophysics	granulate	solicitude	

1. He wanders about all day, lives like a _____.
2. Big boys sometimes _____ over the younger pupils.
3. The syrup would not _____ properly.
4. I was touched by the teacher's _____.
5. The sailor kept a detailed _____ of his daily activities.

Group 3

pilfer	cathartic	incinerate	acerbic
desiccate	italicize	connive	

1. Crying is a _____ release.
2. The guards were suspected of _____ at the prisoner's escape.
3. The light bulb was part of a cache _____ from the hotel.
4. Such garbage must be _____ at the hospital.
5. The song filled with soaring melodies built around _____ lyrics.

Group 4

churlish	blithe	nadir	monogamy
anion	jocular	statuary	

1. She made a joke in a _____ voice.
2. It seems _____ to complain such a nice waiter.
3. That _____ comedy we enjoyed yesterday is the best comedy we saw in years.
4. In contrast with the aristocrats who often had more than one wife, the lower class people practiced _____.
5. Both unfortunately and fortunately, they had reached the _____ of their sufferings.

Group 5

aerate	thunderbolt	despot	commiserate
nonchalant	congeal	ostracize	

1. _____ your lawn to allow it to breathe and absorb water better.
2. The poet has been ridiculed, _____, and persecuted for centuries.
3. She did not exult in her rival's fall, but, on the contrary, _____ her.
4. He gave a _____ shrug, showing that he did not care about her miserable story at all.
5. The blood had _____ into blobs.

Group 6

adulation	desultory	trenchant	tremulous
compunction	fatuous	hummingbird	

1. A few people were left, dancing in a _____ fashion.

2. The police can feel the fear in Barbara's _____ voice.
3. He had no _____ about behaving blasphemously.
4. She heard angry voices, not loud, yet certainly _____.
5. He found it difficult to cope with the _____ of the fans.

Group 7

endorphin	gibberish	demystify	desecrate

mote	claustrophobia	procrastinate

1. This book attempts to _____ technology using simple words and everyday examples.
2. The faded memory feels like the tiniest _____ of dust.
3. More than 300 ancient graves are _____.
4. Under the effect of the drugs, he talks _____.
5. It won't be on sale at this price for long, so don't _____.

Group 8

snide	sunspot	callus	lugubrious

waddle	waggle	sinuous

1. The river follows a _____ trail through the forest.
2. The _____ divorce lawyer only wants to make some easy money from the case.
3. Mary _____ a glass at them to say hi.
4. She is unhappy about the loss, not _____ yet.
5. Three baby geese _____ across the road.

Group 9

myopia	waistline	vitriol	membranous

subterfuge	transmute	alacrity

1. Having been on diet for months, he finally managed to eliminate inches from the _____.
2. The raw material of his experience was _____ into stories.
3. The officer's lie is a disreputable _____.
4. Historians have been criticized for their _____ in treating modern science as a western phenomenon.
5. She accepted the invitation for being the bridesmaid with _____.

Group 10

apprise	monomer	amorous	hodgepodge

submersible	conflagration	vertigo

1. I thought it right to _____ Chris of what had happened.
2. Rob's living room was a _____ of modern furniture and antiques.
3. The steep narrow stairs give me _____.
4. The _____ spread rapidly through the wooden buildings.
5. She rejected his _____ advances desultorily.

Answers — P130

Word List 8

Group 1

obfuscate	chivalrous	rambunctious	outvote
transfiguration	anatomist	gibe	

1. His _____ treatment of her wife led to the demise of their marriage.
2. The director afraid that some cynics in the media might _____ at his new movie.
3. His _____ treatment of women earned him the reputation for being a gentleman.
4. It is more likely to _____ people than to enlighten them.
5. In this light the junk undergoes a _____; it shines.

Group 2

fulsome	stinger	flotsam	omnivorous
despoil	firmament	toady	

1. They are almost embarrassingly _____ in their appreciation.
2. Mr.Woods is one of the great stars in the American golfing _____.
3. She can imagine him _____ to his rich clients.
4. The writer is also an _____ reader, reading everything from product instructions to serious literatures.
5. The church was _____ of its marble wall covering.

Group 3

tardy	deify	endothermic	dewy
cranium	obdurate	soporific	

1. His _____ parents refused to make any change to the living room.
2. The _____ of our prehistoric ancestor is displaying in the museum.
3. The motion of the train had a somewhat _____ effect; it helped her fall in sleep.
4. Please forgive my _____ reply; I have been delayed by some incident.
5. She was _____ by the early Romans as a fertility goddess.

Group 4

mellifluous	unsullied	carapace	fractionate
matriculate	cantankerous	monger	

1. The diva's voice was _____ and smooth.
2. His bad manner showed exactly how _____ a person he is.
3. She cherished her _____ reputation.
4. She has been _____ into her dream school.
5. In the post-Watergate era, power has been _____ on Capitol Hill.

Group 5

headwind	putrid	missal	malediction
dilatory	miasma	prescience	

1. They resorted to _____ procedural tactics, forcing a postponement of peach talks.
2. A _____ of despair rose from the black workshops.
3. The _____ of the evil neighbor did not ruin her day.
4. With extraordinary _____, Jung actually predicted the Nazi eruption.
5. The _____ smells from the slaughterhouses make me want to vomit.

Group 6

aspersion	paleoanthropologist	nonplus	unpick
surreptitious	voyeur		peevish

1. Don't worry; I don't think anyone is casting _____ on you.
2. Bojack was _____ by such an odd question.
3. I _____ the seams of his trousers.
4. In order to avoid aspersion, the celebrity couple carried on a _____ affair.
5. All this makes Steve fretful and _____.

Group 7

bate	supercilious	phlegmatic	centenarian
adsorbent	salable	debauch	

1. That _____ lady has no interest in entry-level middle class.
2. Public morals have been _____ by some evil criminals.
3. To his dying day he _____ his breath a little when he told the story.
4. I come from a very emotional family—I can't remember one _____ moment from my childhood.
5. Activated charcoal is a kind of _____ material used by some to absorb unpleasant smell.

Group 8

querulous	protean	prickle	callow
astringent	torpor	reprobate	

1. The feeling of _____ lingered for months until there is only one week left for the exam.
2. Shostakovich was a remarkably _____ composer, one at home in a wide range of styles.
3. Even the most _____ patients failed to upset the patient young nurse.
4. She toyed with the emotions of Langton when he was a _____ and insecure young man.
5. I hate the way the fibers _____ my skin.

Group 9

millennial	effrontery	pugnacious	malodorous
pentagon	woeful	crocodilian	

1. The politicians are becoming more _____ as the final election approaching.
2. Several tenants in the building had complained about the _____ apartment on the second floor.
3. One juror had the _____ to challenge the coroner's decision.
4. The police response was _____ inadequate.
5. _____ are distinguished by long jaws, short legs, and a powerful tail.

Group 10

cataclysm	cabal	sadism	sycophant
evanescent	iconoclast	chicanery	

1. I thought you wanted a competent assistant, not a nodding _____.
2. The project is operating on an _____ budget.
3. The _____ of the First World War destroyed numerous families.
4. Ms. Farber is an underhanded person who schemes corruption and political _____ behind closed doors.
5. Idealists are _____ in a money culture.

Answers — P131

Word List 9

Group 1

diablo	slate	tract	pulpit

autodidact	anesthetic	scathing	

1. He's a self-proclaimed _____ who learns best through self-teaching.
2. Such provisions have received _____ criticism from privacy advocates.
3. The female duck's reproductive _____ is a long helical passage with branching dean-end tunnels.
4. The doctor gave him the stitches without an _____.
5. To the right of the house there was a _____ path that led away into the pines.

Group 2

betoken	deoxyribonucleic acid	roster	plaster

corpulence	minutiae	gut-level	

1. The blossoms _____ spring, but the bare trees with a few red leaves seem autumnal.
2. The woman was bigger than them, with a horse's _____, and from what I could tell, a man's height.
3. I was learning to decipher the _____ of posture and the fluctuations in facial muscles.
4. The yellowed _____ overhead was split by a lightning bolt fracture.
5. _____ playing is mastery born from a lifetime of discipline and thought.

Group 3

unfetter	splinter	photon	misgiving

yolk	railing	litany	

1. The team blamed its losses on a _____ of injuries.
2. I felt some _____ about his ability to do the job.
3. When I reached the fifth floor I leaned over the _____, hoping to relieve a bit of the nausea.
4. The place is driven by a distinctly Utopian desire to _____, not restrict, and to champion individuality and idiosyncrasy.
5. The party had begun to _____ into factions.

Group 4

binge	overarching	blazing	pike

solute	predisposition	comestible	

1. There are studies that show _____ drinking can actually kill brain cells.
2. It's time for him to come up with a real _____ strategy to defeat.
3. The _____ logs in the fireplace cast a warm glow on our holiday party.
4. His degree of success and fame encouraged his _____ towards feelings of self-importance.
5. Supposedly the water would remember its infinitely diluted _____ better that way.

Group 5

ectotherm	squeal	cant	dimwitted

seedling	snare	perch	

1. The liberal case against all censorship is often _____.

2. The _____ waiter broke the glass.
3. "Let me go," she _____.
4. They caught fish and _____ seabirds.
5. The pigeon is _____ on the roof.

Group 6

Pleistocene	flick	duplicitous	folklorist
thermophile	pier	shoal	

1. He _____ the light switch on as he went into the room.
2. Critics point out Tehran's behavior has always been inconsistent, secretive and _____.
3. A _____ of salmon jumped for their lives and fled this way.
4. John was an early public _____ who specialized in collecting cowboy songs.
5. Tie the boat up at the _____.

Group 7

drab	maladroit	kayak	petrified
corsage	overlying	pinnacle	

1. There were tears in his eyes and he looked _____.
2. Thomas Paine lived in rented house, ate little, and wore _____ clothes.
3. The singer has reached the _____ of success.
4. There is a river where you might even paddle a _____ or float a raft.
5. The dancer was _____ and unbalanced.

Group 8

buff	estuary	scheming	gristle
entourage	gene-sequencing	level-headed	

1. I use a cleaner to _____ the floor to give it a shine but the scratches are too noticeable.

2. He wasn't with an _____. He was alone.
3. The city sits on the shores of a deep _____ where the Hudson River meets the Atlantic Ocean.
4. He has another _____ to cheat people out of their money.
5. You need a _____ assessment of the problem.

Group 9

nail down	mass protest	extant	dogged
rubble	millennia	pickle	

1. There is no _____ copy of the Super Bowl I television broadcast; nobody bothered to keep the tapes.
2. Her _____ efforts eventually paid off.
3. The earthquake reduced the whole town to _____.
4. Around 10000 demonstrators are expected to take part in a _____ to express anger at the financial burdens.
5. The year 2000 was celebrated as the beginning of the third _____.

Group 10

raisin	dab	strenuous	whelm
cacophonous	resorb	spruce	

1. Avoid all _____ exercise until the sprain heals.
2. A swimmer was _____ in a raging storm.
3. She _____ at her eyes with a handkerchief.
4. There is a slim, _____ man in a tailor-made business suit.
5. The sounds of barking dogs and sirens added to the _____ on the streets.

Answers — P132

Word List 10

Group 1

pernicious	savant	careen	tawdry
sanctify	parson	slouch	

1. She was so exhausted that she walked with a _____.
2. The sled _____ as it barreled down the hill.
3. She thinks television has a _____ influence on our children.
4. Christopher is a mathematical _____ with a photographic memory.
5. The priest _____ their marriage.

Group 2

hemline	inure	subservient	raze
infestation	aspen	figurehead	

1. The hardship of army training _____ her to the rigors of desert warfare.
2. The theory makes freedom _____ to control.
3. He was likely a mere _____, unable to capitalize upon his abilities or realize his dreams.
4. If we enter Laconia, we will _____ it to ground.
5. In desperation, we called in an exterminator because the house was _____ with ants.

Group 3

probity	dreg	pungent	abrogate
scallop	tangerine	scarecrow	

1. I remember the enormous size of that fire and the _____ smell of smoke from the burning house.
2. The president _____ an old law.
3. The defense attorney questioned the _____ of the witness.
4. His clothes are as ragged as a _____.
5. _____ settled at the bottom of the container.

Group 4

facile	broach	pittance	foment
ejaculation	elk	whiplash	

1. Although many of the poorest now get some kind of governmental support, it is only a _____.
2. If women were not remembered by the new American government, they would _____ a rebellion.
3. After the discussion, she _____ an idea.
4. This problem needs more than just a _____ solution.
5. The force of the impact had _____ the man's head.

Group 5

pique	beehive	quandary	sled
synopsis	accordion	agronomist	

1. I am in a _____ about whether I should try to repair my computer or buy a new one.
2. After a moment of _____, the senator responded calmly to his accusers.
3. The _____ suggested growing rice on the dried river bed.
4. I stuck my hand in the _____ and then was stung three times.

5. I don't need to know every little plot twist; just give me a _____ of the movie.

Group 6

incandescent	hedonism	expropriate	slumber
rapacious	quizzical	squalor	

1. She _____ for hours while the train rolled on.
2. They lived in _____ and disease.
3. Government plans to _____ farmland.
4. The speaker is _____ with righteous anger over the treatment of the refugees.
5. _____ corporations replace full-time workers with part-time ones in order to cut down on both wages and benefits.

Group 7

marigold	ignominious	gargantuan	piquant
buzzard	penitent	amble	

1. They _____ down the road.
2. He was _____ about his mistake.
3. The prison guards degraded themselves with their inhumane, _____ treatment of the prisoners.
4. He served the fish with a _____ sauce.
5. After exercise, you will have a _____ appetite.

Group 8

plunger	petulant	cornucopia	pancreas
blustery	sanctimonious	percolate	

1. The water gradually _____ down through the sands.
2. The market is a _____ of fruits and vegetables.

3. A _____ and fussy man is always blaming everyone else for his problems.
4. A winter gale _____ against the sides of the house.
5. The death of Steve Jobs from _____ cancer added another name to the list of celebrities who have died as a result of cancer.

Group 9

glut	androgen	smudge	aver
amphitheater	impugn	indenture	

1. Her movies have been scrutinized and _____ by critics.
2. Landowners tried to get their estates cultivated by _____ labors.
3. Don't _____ the picture with your dirty hands.
4. She _____ that solitude was necessary for creative work.
5. The roads are _____ with cars.

Group 10

snuggle	enmesh	parsimony	guillotine
mope	nemesis	hap	

1. These young men were _____ in difficulties when they started a new business.
2. Will Harry Potter finally defeat his _____, Voldemort?
3. Her _____ was so extreme that she'd walk five miles to the store to save a few cents on gas.
4. The boy _____ close to his mother.
5. We were in a rush, but the Sunder driver in front of us was just _____ along.

Answers — P133

答案 Answers

预热级

Word List 1

Group 1		Group 6	
1. 稳定的；恒定的	2. 靠近；来临	1. 客观的	2. 卓越的
3. 关键的	4. 最重要的	3. 虐待	4. 评价
5. 排除	6. 怀疑	5. 运动	6. 强度
7. 倾斜		7. 事件	
1. suspected	2. constant	1. motion	2. assess
3. crucial	4. approached	3. remarkable	4. objective
5. principal		5. episode	
Group 2		**Group 7**	
1. 证明…是正当的	2. 供选择的	1. 情节	2. 试验
3. 阶段	4. 传统	3. 容纳的能力	4. 工序，过程
5. 摆动	6. 重要的；大量的	5. 改变	6. 准则
7. 产量；出产		7. 保持	
1. substantial	2. convention	1. plot	2. criterion
3. yielded	4. justify	3. capacity	4. alter
5. Alternative		5. Retain	
Group 3		**Group 8**	
1. 察觉；感知	2. 一致的	1. 工具	2. 广泛的
3. 附属	4. 包含	3. 保险	4. 提及
5. 位于…之下	6. 委员会	5. 保守的	6. 恳求
7. 革新		7. 承诺	
1. consistent	2. incorporate	1. reference	2. extensive
3. perceive/perceived	4. innovation	3. implement	4. commitment
5. underlie		5. conservative	
Group 4		**Group 9**	
1. 萧条；沮丧	2. 里面的	1. 存在	2. 储备
3. 猜想	4. 核心	3. 痕迹	4. 使显露
5. 变化	6. 区分	5. 扔；抛	6. 消除
7. 观点，视角		7. 外在的	
1. core	2. distinguish	1. external	2. presence
3. perspective	4. assume	3. reserve	4. expose
5. variation		5. eliminate	
Group 5		**Group 10**	
1. 强制实行	2. 极其重要的	1. 切开	2. 庄园；地产
3. 品种，类型	4. 控制；主导	3. 塑料(的)	4. 一排
5. 设立	6. 事业	5. 抗议	6. 出现
7. 部队		7. 干涉	
1. strains	2. dominated	1. protest	2. emerged/emerges
3. troop	4. vital	3. split	4. plastic
5. impose		5. intervention	

Word List 2

Group 1	
1. 导致	2. 使…适合
3. 诉诸于	4. 交易
5. 抓住	6. 支持
7. 泵	
1. grab	2. prompted
3. championed/champions	4. resort
5. transaction	

Group 2	
1. 全面的	2. 一致
3. 搅动	4. 恐慌
5. 热情	6. 脏乱
7. 深思	
1. comprehensive	2. passion
3. consensus	4. panic
5. reflection	

Group 3	
1. 缠绕	2. 露齿笑
3. 种族的	4. 容器
5. 汲取液体	6. 海豹
7. 饲养	
1. rears	2. vessel
3. twisted	4. grin
5. Racial	

Group 4	
1. 组成	2. 暴露
3. 归于	4. 冒险
5. 取出	6. 整合
7. 实体	
1. constitute	2. venture
3. integration	4. attribute
5. Exposure	

Group 5	
1. 间隔	2. 温和的，适量的
3. 领土	4. 实施
5. 有争议的	6. 根本的
7. 一击	
1. implementation	2. radical
3. interval	4. controversial
5. Moderate	

Group 6	
1. 平行的	2. 快速转动
3. 结盟；盟友	4. 复合的
5. 无辜的	6. 洞穴
7. 内部	
1. compound	2. spins
3. interior	4. ally
5. innocent	

Group 7	
1. 酸	2. 估计
3. 维持	4. 聚集
5. 查问	6. 研讨会
7. 刺激	
1. reckoned	2. sustained
3. inquiries	4. seminar
5. clustered/cluster	

Group 8	
1. 分散	2. 目录
3. 叙事(的)	4. 分开的
5. 经历	6. 横梁
7. 提供	
1. distinct	2. narrative
3. scattering	4. render
5. undergo	

Group 9	
1. 超过	2. 激励
3. 压榨	4. 沉积(物)
5. 调节	6. 引发
7. 限制	
1. deposit	2. exceeded/exceeds
3. incentive	4. constraint
5. trigger	

Group 10	
1. 解散	2. 随后的
3. 清醒的，有意识的	4. 假设的
5. 动态(的)	6. 增加
7. 情况	
1. dynamic	2. mounting
3. subsequent	4. scenario
5. dismiss	

Word List 3

Group 1	
1. 铝	2. 感觉；知觉
3. 部分的	4. 集体的
5. 标本；样本	6. 实证的
7. 修剪	
1. collective	2. partial
3. sensation	4. clipping
5. empirical	

Group 2	
1. 使嵌入，使插入	2. 限制
3. 光谱	4. (不愉快事情的)开始
5. (原子或细胞)核	6. 线
7. 美学的	
1. embedding	2. confines
3. spectrum	4. onset
5. thread	

Group 3	
1. 特点	2. 捆
3. 复杂的	4. 操作
5. 暗喻	6. 加强；巩固
7. 辩论；论文	
1. metaphor	2. elaborate
3. reinforce	4. manipulate
5. trait	

Group 4	
1. 使用手册	2. 描绘
3. 粗糙的	4. 概念的；想法上的
5. 繁殖	6. 自发的；自然的
7. 颗粒	
1. conceptual	2. crude
3. portray	4. manual
5. Spontaneous	

Group 5	
1. 免疫的	2. 传播
3. 评论	4. 补偿
5. 不相关的	6. 开始
7. 想出	
1. conceive	2. commentary
3. transmitted	4. compensate
5. immune	

Group 6	
1. 放映	2. 巨大；规模
3. 缺陷	4. 合并
5. 方言	6. 狭缝；槽沟；投币口
7. 模糊的	
1. defect	2. projection
3. magnitude	4. merged
5. dialect	

Group 7	
1. 商品	2. 辐射
3. 困境	4. 遮掩，隐藏
5. 像	6. 古怪的
7. 有磁性的	
1. dilemma	2. commodity
3. obscure	4. bizarre
5. resemble	

Group 8	
1. 喷	2. 大块
3. 静止的	4. 精英
5. 领域	6. 殖民地的
7. 逐渐破坏；削弱	
1. bulk	2. elite
3. static	4. sprayed
5. sphere	

Group 9	
1. 强度	2. 聚集；合计，总计
3. 仪式	4. 侵略，入侵
5. 紧密的	6. 邻近的
7. 诊断；断定	
1. ritual	2. aggregate
3. adjacent	4. invade
5. intensity	

Group 10	
1. 原始的	2. 盆地
3. 含蓄的	4. 纤维
5. 腐烂	6. 明确的，清楚的
7. 融合	
1. implicit	2. fusion
3. basin	4. decaying
5. Primitive	

Word List 4

Group 1	
1. 周年纪念日	2. 授权
3. 策略	4. 裸露的
5. 大约的	6. 要素
7. 引起	
1. ingredient	2. tactic
3. anniversary	4. bare
5. authorize	

Group 2	
1. 流	2. 代理人；出庭律师
3. 恶化；降低	4. 消除；淘汰
5. 水库	6. 术语
7. 慷慨的	
1. elimination	2. terminology
3. reservoir	4. degrades
5. attorney	

Group 3	
1. 引发	2. 高度
3. 视力的	4. 半径；半径范围
5. 原子的	6. 停止，结束
7. 违反	
1. atomic	2. altitude
3. optical	4. sparked
5. cease	

Group 4	
1. 块，片	2. 易受伤害的
3. 对应的人或物	4. 提供
5. 围绕	6. 振奋
7. 下降	
1. vulnerable	2. descend
3. patch	4. accommodate
5. counterpart	

Group 5	
1. 祈求	2. 独有的；排外的
3. 捕食性动物	4. 强迫
5. 互相矛盾的	6. 必然的，不可避免的
7. 热的	
1. compelled	2. exclusive
3. inevitable	4. predator
5. contradictory	

Group 6	
1. 停止	2. 与…矛盾
3. 破裂，折断；骨折	4. 取回
5. 专利(权)	6. 任意的
7. 主流	
1. contradict	2. patent
3. withdrawal	4. halted
5. arbitrary	

Group 7	
1. 牧师	2. 接待处；款待
3. 减少	4. 加速
5. 忽略	6. 带领
7. 黎明	
1. overlook	2. diminished
3. acceleration	4. reception
5. dawn	

Group 8	
1. 指定；指派	2. 雕塑
3. 绝望的；极渴望的	4. 逃离
5. 重新开始	6. 看似合理的
7. 毁灭	
1. sculpture	2. designated
3. desperate	4. plausible
5. fled	

Group 9	
1. 撤退	2. 朋友
3. 沉淀物	4. 酷刑；折磨
5. 速度	6. 质子
7. 愤怒	
1. retreat	2. companion
3. velocity	4. sediment
5. rage	

Group 10	
1. 创建者	2. 摩擦
3. 测量	4. 认为，视作
5. 不重要的	6. 配方
7. 正直；完整	
1. gauge	2. friction
3. integrity	4. founders
5. deem/deemed	

Word List 5

Group 1	
1. 可疑的	2. 故意的
3. 夸大	4. 使胆寒
5. 突然消失	6. 来自异国的
7. 猛烈的	
1. vanished	2. deliberate
3. exotic	4. suspicious
5. appalls	

Group 2	
1. 自传；自传文学	2. 拖运；拖拉
3. 木材	4. 混合物
5. 游行；阅兵	6. 淹没
7. 使固定	
1. parade	2. anchor
3. drowned	4. hybrid
5. hauled	

Group 3	
1. 精美的	2. 猜测
3. 渴望	4. 内在的，固有的
5. 前任	6. 对抗
7. 远征；探险队	
1. predecessors	2. aspiration
3. confrontation	4. speculate
5. delicate	

Group 4	
1. 各自的	2. 操控
3. 居住；沉湎于	4. 猛增
5. 跳跃	6. 证实
7. 抵消	
1. testify	2. dwell
3. offset	4. respective
5. maneuver	

Group 5	
1. 砍	2. 群
3. 使分心	4. 扭曲
5. 谨慎的，小心的	6. 坚持不懈的
7. 干扰，妨碍	
1. cautious	2. distracted
3. persistent	4. distorted
5. interference	

Group 6	
1. 完好无缺的	2. 混乱；混沌
3. 阐明；照亮	4. 浸泡
5. 收据；收到	6. 结合
7. 展开	
1. intact	2. illuminate
3. chaos	4. conjunction
5. unfold	

Group 7	
1. 草地，草坪	2. 拱形
3. 演替；继任	4. 裁决，裁定
5. 汇编	6. 召唤
7. 冲刷；脸红	
1. succession	2. compile
3. verdict	4. summoned
5. flushed	

Group 8	
1. 穿透	2. 推迟
3. 毁坏	4. 证实
5. 取来	6. 坚持
7. 磨碎	
1. postponed	2. verified
3. penetrate	4. wrecked
5. ground	

Group 9	
1. 粉碎	2. 树干；躯干
3. 亲密的	4. 巨大的
5. 提供；装饰	6. 处理
7. 限制	
1. furnish	2. disposal
3. intimate	4. restraints
5. shattered	

Group 10	
1. 大教堂	2. 检查
3. 斗争；主张	4. 击碎
5. 热情；热烈的	6. 企业家
7. 硬的，僵硬的	
1. inspected	2. contended
3. stiff	4. entrepreneur
5. smashed	

Word List 6

Group 1	
1. 下降	2. 合唱队
3. 引用，援引	4. 必要的(事)
5. 分散；使散开	6. 连续的
7. 省的；地方性的	
1. consecutive	2. imperative
3. invoked	4. disperse
5. provincial	

Group 2	
1. 美丽动人的	2. 缺陷
3. 酿制啤酒	4. 争吵；大惊小怪
5. 烈火	6. 恢复；复兴
7. 怀疑的	
1. gorgeous	2. revival
3. skeptical	4. drawback
5. blaze	

Group 3	
1. 倾向于	2. 圣地
3. 羡慕	4. 可行的
5. 肋骨	6. 废除
7. 卓越的	
1. feasible	2. abolishing
3. envy	4. prone
5. supreme	

Group 4	
1. 危害	2. 抛弃；放弃
3. 散文	4. 城市的
5. 圣徒	6. 体现，使具体化
7. 瘟疫；折磨	
1. embody	2. discarding
3. civic	4. endangered
5. plague	

Group 5	
1. 陶瓷	2. 大厦
3. 堆	4. 使需要，必需
5. 多变的	6. 加强
7. 缓冲，缓解	
1. intensified/intensify	2. heap
3. cushion	4. volatile
5. entails	

Group 6	
1. 透明的	2. 发芽
3. 背心；马甲	4. 摄取量
5. 便于携带的	6. 远足；涉足
7. 狂怒的	
1. furious	2. intake
3. portable	4. excursion
5. transparent	

Group 7	
1. 窒息，阻塞	2. 缓冲
3. 碎片；残骸	4. 灯泡
5. 强壮的；坚定的	6. 兼容的；相符的
7. 空着的；空缺的	
1. robust	2. choke
3. debris	4. compatible
5. vacant	

Group 8	
1. 粘附；遵守	2. 纵容，放纵
3. 详细叙述	4. 松脆的
5. 帆布	6. 臭名昭著的
7. 海盗	
1. adhere	2. crisp
3. notorious	4. recounted
5. indulge	

Group 9	
1. 刺	2. 手提包，钱包
3. 引出	4. 溅起
5. 谴责	6. 低估
7. 姿势	
1. underestimate	2. splashed
3. elicit	4. denounce
5. posture	

Group 10	
1. 灾难的	2. 到期
3. 颅骨	4. 犁；耕地
5. 市政的	6. 肥料
7. 皱眉	
1. disastrous	2. frowned
3. expired	4. fertilizer
5. Municipal	

Word List 7

Group 1	
1. 污染	2. 灭绝
3. 到达顶点	4. 孤独的
5. 运输	6. 水汽
7. 拥挤	
1. extinction	2. solitary
3. contaminate	4. transit
5. culminate	

Group 2	
1. 碰撞	2. 叙述者
3. 驱逐	4. 喘气
5. 永恒的	6. 喧闹；忙乱
7. 碎石；砂砾	
1. collision	2. eternal
3. expel	4. gasp
5. narrator's	

Group 3	
1. (使) 入伍	2. 恐龙
3. 面纱	4. 反复出现
5. 肥沃的	6. 阻碍
7. 霜冻	
1. enlisted	2. fertile
3. dinosaur	4. veil
5. recur	

Group 4	
1. 复制；使加倍	2. 缠结
3. 痉挛	4. 静止不动的
5. 揭幕；揭露	6. 反抗
7. 使等同；相同	
1. defy	2. duplicate
3. tangled	4. unveil
5. equate	

Group 5	
1. 橄榄球的四分卫	2. 削弱；瘸子
3. 鼓掌	4. 后裔；子孙
5. 繁荣的	6. 羞辱
7. 使疏远，离间	
1. applauded	2. cripple
3. descendants	4. humiliated
5. prosperous	

Group 6	
1. 授权	2. 修女
3. 立体声(音响)	4. 爆发
5. 宽敞的	6. 理解
7. 剧烈的	
1. drastic	2. erupted/erupts
3. spacious	4. empower
5. comprehend	

Group 7	
1. 自传	2. 开发，开采
3. 无效的	4. 珊瑚
5. 强大的	6. 辨别
7. 抛弃	
1. discern	2. formidable
3. Autobiography	4. exploitation
5. void	

Group 8	
1. 强有力的	2. 寄生虫
3. 到来，出现	4. 分类
5. 地壳	6. 气味
7. 压缩	
1. potent	2. advent
3. categorize	4. compress
5. odor	

Group 9	
1. 海底的	2. 戏剧性的
3. 流行的	4. 灶台
5. 人口普查	6. 宗族
7. 分发	
1. theatrical	2. prevalent
3. dispensed	4. Submarine
5. census	

Group 10	
1. 摘录	2. 设备
3. 通勤	4. 外交
5. 亲密	6. 闪烁
7. 超过	
1. intimacy	2. apparatus
3. blink	4. excerpt
5. diplomacy	

Word List 8

Group 1	
1. 吸入	2. 缺点
3. 学徒	4. 阻碍
5. 欺骗	6. 发芽
7. 想象	
1. hinders/hindered	2. shortcomings
3. deception	4. apprentice
5. Inhale	

Group 2	
1. 小薄片	2. 全包括的
3. 娱乐的	4. 动力
5. 推进	6. 混乱的
7. 根除，根绝	
1. propelled	2. recreational
3. inclusive	4. impetus
5. chaotic	

Group 3	
1. 必不可少的	2. 解开
3. 阁楼	4. 邻近，附近
5. 推荐，称赞	6. 专断的；权威的
7. 贪婪	
1. unravel	2. vicinity
3. authoritative	4. indispensable
5. Greed	

Group 4	
1. 突然的	2. 可再生的
3. 公共的	4. 本质的，必要的
5. 冰川	6. 指南针
7. 胶囊	
1. intrinsic	2. abrupt
3. communal	4. compass
5. renewable	

Group 5	
1. 使漂白；漂白剂	2. 使黯然失色
3. 注意，留意	4. 暗指
5. 污染	6. 催化剂
7. 熔岩	
1. heed	2. catalyst
3. bleach	4. eclipsed
5. contamination	

Group 6	
1. 花岗岩	2. 盘起
3. 有危险的	4. 无情的，残忍的
5. 扩散	6. 贮存物；隐藏处
7. 背景	
1. hazardous	2. ruthless
3. backdrop	4. Granite
5. Coil	

Group 7	
1. 腺	2. 粗糙的
3. 浸泡；沉浸于	4. 多年生的，四季不断的
5. 挖掘；开凿	6. 优越
7. 开垦	
1. immersed	2. coarse
3. superiority	4. perennial
5. excavate	

Group 8	
1. 缄默的	2. 坑，火山口
3. 使形象化；预想	4. 靠近
5. 诱使；怂恿	6. 证明
7. 认真的	
1. mute	2. adjoin
3. attest	4. entice
5. visualized	

Group 9	
1. 承受住	2. 恶化
3. 异常	4. 狂暴；狂怒
5. 死，死亡	6. 蒸发
7. 巨大的，庞大的	
1. anomaly	2. withstand
3. evaporate	4. frenzy
5. deterioration	

Group 10	
1. 居住者	2. 缓解，减轻
3. 铭刻	4. 峡谷
5. 讨厌或累人的工作	6. 使不可信
7. 使浓缩	
1. mitigate	2. occupants
3. chore	4. imprints
5. discredit	

Word List 9

Group 1	
1. 最重要的	2. 有远见的；空想的
3. 花瓣	4. 关键的
5. 缴…的械	6. 水生的
7. 给…蒙上阴影	
1. overshadowed	2. paramount
3. aquatic	4. pivotal
5. visionary	

Group 2	
1. 使显贵，抬高…的身价	2 渗透，弥漫
3 绝缘；隔热	4. 贯穿，横穿
5. 意译	6. 悲观的
7. 狂欢节	
1. permeated	2. dignified
3. pessimistic	4. paraphrase
5. insulate	

Group 3	
1. 求助；手段	2. 小行星
3. 短暂的；暂居的	4. 抵消；中和
5. 避开	6. 星座
7. 殖民	
1. transient	2. colonized
3. recourse	4. shunned
5. neutralized	

Group 4	
1. 嘲弄	2. 潮汐的
3. 养育	4. 罪犯，罪魁祸首
5. 交谈，谈话	6. 精力；魄力
7. 伪装	
1. camouflage	2. culprits
3. vigor	4. ridiculed
5. nourish	

Group 5	
1. 无菌的；不孕的	2. 影响发展的
3. 无能的；没有行为能力的	4. 可忽略不计的
5. 着陆	6. 推断
7. 整数	
1. negligible	2. deduce
3. touchdown	4. Sterile
5. incompetent	

Group 6	
1. 死亡，枯萎	2. 强壮的
3. 怡人的	4. 闯入
5. 即兴创作	6. 可行性；可能性
7. 解除；溶解	
1. perish	2. feasibility
3. intruding	4. improvise
5. agreeable	

Group 7	
1. 类似的	2. 添加的
3. 使贫穷，使枯竭	4. 边缘；周长
5. 衰落；月亏	6. 必要的
7. 遵守	
1. waning	2. impoverished
3. requisite	4. conform
5. analogous	

Group 8	
1. 按年代顺序排列的	2. 淹没
3. 无数，极大数量	4. 麻木的，失去知觉的
5. 长方形的	6. 勇敢的
7. 纬度；自由度	
1. myriad	2. courageous
3. numb	4. chronological
5. latitude	

Group 9	
1. 垂直的；探究	2. 减缓；妨碍
3. 灵长目动物	4. 无意中听到
5. 狂热；疯狂	6. 加快
7. 百科全书	
1. hasten	2. overheard
3. plumbing	4. retarded
5. mania	

Group 10	
1. 融化，融解	2. 挥霍的；昂贵的
3. 世界性的	4. 洞穴；藏身处
5. 火炉，熔炉	6. 清淡的；乏味的
7. 解释的	
1. cosmopolitan	2. thaws
3. explanatory	4. extravagant
5. bland	

Word List 10

Group 1	
1. 耐用；持久	2. 暴君
3. 描绘	4. 坚持不懈的
5. 忠诚	6. 呼气
7. 偏离	
1. delineated	2. durability
3. deviated	4. fidelity
5. diligent	

Group 2	
1. 点亮着的；飞落	2 不太可能的
3 祖先	4. 平静的；安静的
5. 雄鹿；后部的	6. 使纠缠
7. 象征；符号	
1. tranquil	2. entangle
3. hind	4. alighted
5. ancestry	

Group 3	
1. 不死的	2. 荒凉的
3. 宏伟的，堂皇的	4. 朗诵会；演奏会
5. 费力的	6. 谚语
7. 巨大的	
1. immortal	2. arduous
3. colossal	4. desolate
5. recital	

Group 4	
1. 未预料到的	2. 使湿透；滂沱大雨
3. 猜测	4. 破译
5. 壮丽，庄严，宏伟	6. 有洞察力的
7. 排斥	
1. surmise	2. drench
3. unforeseen	4. insightful
5. repel	

Group 5	
1. 费力，努力	2. 零星的；偶发的
3. 分解；腐烂	4. 文盲的，不识字的
5. 强迫	6. 绘画的；图示的
7. 早期的；原始的	
1. rudimentary	2. coerce
3. exerted	4. illiterate
5. decompose	

Group 6	
1. 两栖动物	2. 蛤蜊
3. 大提琴	4. 重新考虑
5. 腹部	6. 地图册
7. 咏叹调，独唱曲	
1. cello	2. amphibian
3. atlas	4. abdomen
5. reassess	

Group 7	
1. 全盛时期	2. 小数
3. 细致的，一丝不苟的	4. 可食用的
5. 喷射	6. 不能肯定下结论的
7. 小口地吃	
1. inconclusive	2. meticulous
3. heyday	4. eject
5. edible	

Group 8	
1. 残留；吃剩	2. 主旨，要点
3. 蚕食，侵占	4. 率直的
5. 原始的；崭新的	6. 改变
7. 芳香的	
1. encroach	2. mutation
3. pristine	4. Leftover
5. candid	

Group 9	
1. 碳酸盐	2. 典范的，可仿效的
3. 天上的，天空的	4. 有分歧的
5. 发光的；明亮的	6. 使困惑
7. 成直角的；直立的	
1. exemplary	2. divisive
3. mystify	4. celestial
5. luminous	

Group 10	
1. 修饰；装饰	2. 神经学上的，神经病学的
3. 使困惑	4. 芳香的
5. 暗示	6. 间歇的，断断续续的
7. [化学]氮	
1. perplex	2. embellish
3. intermittent	4. allusion
5. neurological	

Word List 11

Group 1	
1. 好奇的；爱钻研的	2. 过度使用
3. 南极洲	4. 组成；弥补
5. 有趣的，搞笑的	6. 堆积
7. 人造的	
1. overuse	2. inquisitive
3. artificial	4. piling up
5. make up	

Group 2	
1. 无意的，疏忽的	2. [数]可约分的
3. 星际的	4. 椭圆的
5. 使发生，引起	6. 干旱的
7. 好争论的	
1. inadvertent	2. interstellar
3. arid	4. gives rise to
5. elliptical	

Group 3	
1. 寿命	2. 谨慎的
3. 隔音的	4. 涂层
5. 地热的	6. 可传导的
7. 遗传	
1. soundproof	2. guarded
3. conductive	4. Heredity
5. life span	

Group 4	
1. 陷入；渐渐养成	2. 考虑
3. 宇宙学	4. 瑕疵；玷污，弄脏
5. 使活泼；使生动	6. 可渗透的
7. 剥夺	
1. take into account	2. blemished
3. permeated	4. Cosmology
5. depriving	

Group 5	
1. 生态学家	2. 有偏见的
3. 顶峰；顶点	4. 脊椎
5. 缩小；限制	6. 种族间的
7. 复杂的	
1. peak	2. biased
3. constricted	4. complicated
5. Interracial	

Group 6	
1. 迅速；湍急	2. 轨道的
3. 谜	4. 营养食物；营养提供
5. 无自信；羞怯	6. 推迟；延误
7. 由…引起	
1. enigma	2. rapidity
3. put off	4. diffident
5. orbits	

Group 7	
1. 难以忍受的	2. 可追踪的
3. 游牧民族，游牧部落	4. 副产品；附带结果
5. 忍受	6. 指的是；提到
7. 使压垮，(痛苦而)不知所措	
1. traces	2. devastated
3. refer to	4. put up with
5. nomadic	

Group 8	
1. 严格要求的	2. 脆弱
3. 惋惜	4. 同等回应；回报
5. 道德准则	6. 空想家
7. 有关，在…方面	
1. reciprocate	2. bemoaning
3. in terms of	4. exacting
5. fragile	

Group 9	
1. 自然结果；副产物	2. 立起，倒放
3. 光合作用	4. 持续的
5. 变色	6. 营养不良
7. 不适合居住的；不友好的	
1. photosynthesis	2. malnourishment
3. outgrowth	4. inhospitable
5. enduring	

Group 10	
1. 反击，抨击	2. 说明问题的
3. 足智多谋的	4. [生态]共生
5. 固定的，牢固的	6. 把…改编成戏剧；夸张
7. 沼泽地	
1. resourceful	2. fixed
3. dramatize	4. deprecating
5. telling	

基本级
Word List 1

Group 1	
1. 使沉淀，使落下	2. 补充
3. 最佳的	4. 离散的
5. 代替	6. 使汇聚
7. 转变	
1. converge	2. optimal
3. precipitated	4. transition
5. complement	

Group 2	
1. 灾难；悲剧文学	2. 促进，激励
3. 断言；宣称	4. 悖论
5. 老兵；老手	6. (形成)阵列；排列
7. 酶	
1. paradox	2. boost
3. array	4. alleged
5. veteran	

Group 3	
1. 干涉	2. 假装，模拟，模仿
3. 公正	4. 自由的
5. 热切的	6. 新手
7. 模式化观念；对…形成模式化看法	
1. intervene	2. equity
3. novice	4. simulate
5. stereotype	

Group 4	
1. 有能力的	2. 发音清晰的
3. 染色体	4. 为…提供饮食
5. 保护	6. 务实的
7. 缺陷	
1. conservation	2. articulate
3. defects	4. catered
5. pragmatic	

Group 5	
1. 圆括号；插入语	2. 分配
3. 最终的	4. 参议员
5. 审查(员)	6. 相似
7. 巨大的；深刻的	
1. correspondence	2. profound
3. ultimate	4. allocated
5. censors	

Group 6	
1. 巡航	2. 后代的
3. 鹰	4. 侧面
5. 痛苦	6. 丑闻
7. 混合物；复合的，合成的	
1. descendants	2. scandal
3. facet	4. distress
5. composite	

Group 7	
1. (使)膨胀	2. 意识形态
3. 树篱；防范措施	4. 轮廓
5. 善感的，易受影响的	6. 变体
7. 打扫	
1. ideology	2. contour
3. susceptible	4. variant
5. swelled	

Group 8	
1. 致力于	2. 导师
3. 优美的	4. 前提
5. 外围的	6. 理性的
7. 抗议	
1. dedicate	2. peripheral
3. mentor	4. rational
5. elegant	

Group 9	
1. 不可理解的	2. 嘱咐；规定
3. (使抱)偏见；损害	4. 占支配地位的
5. 倾向	6. 流行病
7. 价值	
1. merit	2. prejudice
3. tendency	4. prescribe
5. unintelligible	

Group 10	
1. 证词	2. 同意
3. 谣言，传闻	4. 慢性的
5. 垄断	6. 分水岭；转折点
7. 做笔录	
1. testimony	2. chronic
3. watershed	4. monopolies
5. consented	

Word List 2

Group 1	
1. 异教团体	2. 违反；破裂
3. 痛苦的	4. 屠杀
5. 揭露	6. 极好的
7. 证明…正当；为…作担保	
1. disclosure	2. slaughter
3. cult	4. breach
5. miserable	

Group 2	
1. 遗产	2. 司法权；管辖权
3. 订购，订阅	4. 坚持不懈的
5. 保证；保修单	6. 巡逻
7. 基准	
1. patrol	2. persistent
3. subscription	4. heritage
5. benchmark	

Group 3	
1. 派系	2. 流放(者)；排除
3. 视情况而定的	4. 壮丽的；极好的
5. 邪恶的	6. 部署
7. 小贩；卖主	
1. deploy	2. exile
3. vicious	4. factions
5. splendid	

Group 4	
1. 发声的	2. (使)附属
3. 护送；护卫	4. 喜爱
5. 回忆录	6. 掩盖
7. 茂盛	
1. disguise	2. escort
3. flourished	4. vocal
5. affiliate	

Group 5	
1. 遗产	2. 接近；边缘
3. 禁止；阻止	4. 后果
5. 将…制定成法律	6. 嘲笑
7. 断言	
1. mocks	2. verge
3. prohibit	4. legacy
5. aftermath	

Group 6	
1. 继承人	2. 弧(度)
3. 有责任的	4. 吐出；喷出
5. 局，处	6. 经常出没于
7. 发生冲突	
1. spits	2. haunts
3. clashed	4. accountable
5. Bureau	

Group 7	
1. 小心，谨慎	2. 蔑视
3. 波动	4. 和解
5. 档案(的)	6. 悲伤；伤心事
7. 人口学的	
1. caution	2. fluctuated
3. contempt	4. reconcile
5. demographic	

Group 8	
1. 发出(声音)；说	2. 殴打，连续猛击
3. 绝望	4. 匍匐
5. 危险	6. 凝视；沉思
7. 哭泣	
1. crawl	2. despair
3. hazard	4. uttered
5. contemplated	

Group 9	
1. 激怒；愤慨	2. 有倾向性的
3. 威吓	4. 强大的
5. 恐惧，担心	6. 过早的；早产的
7. 使有生气	
1. mighty	2. outrage
3. intimidate	4. animated
5. premature	

Group 10	
1. 普通的；通用的	2. 使减小
3. 补偿	4. 赞扬；致意
5. 咆哮	6. 绕行；旁路，支路
7. 猛推；动力	
1. thrust	2. generic
3. roar	4. bypass
5. dimmed	

Word List 3

Group 1	
1. (授予)徽章	2. 混乱
3. 挖掘，开凿	4. 谨慎的
5. 古怪的	6. 授予
7. 重申	
1. turmoil	2. confer
3. eccentric	4. reiterating
5. wary	

Group 2	
1. 慈善的	2. 渴望
3. 补充的，额外的	4. 拖着脚走
5. 啜泣	6. 盘旋
7. 灾难，劫难	
1. aspire	2. shuffles
3. hover	4. charitable
5. catastrophe	

Group 3	
1. 精神失常的	2. 传感器
3. 呼喊	4. 细微差别
5. 假设的，假定的	6. 字面上的
7. 联系	
1. insane	2. hypothetical
3. exclaimed	4. nuance
5. linkage	

Group 4	
1. 呻吟	2. 楔子
3. 临近的	4. 器具
5. 有威望的	6. 含糊不清的
7. 享受，兴趣，喜爱	
1. imminent	2. prestigious
3. relish	4. ambiguous
5. appliances	

Group 5	
1. 仔细考虑	2. 幼虫
3. 威胁	4. 纪念品
5. (持)异议	6. 哀悼；忧伤
7. 威慑	
1. deterred	2. pondered
3. larva	4. dissenting
5. menace	

Group 6	
1. 拦截	2. 排练
3. (使)惊愕	4. 未醉的；清醒的
5. 微型的，小规模的	6. 微光；闪光
7. 使…分开；使孤立	
1. segregated	2. intercepting
3. dismayed	4. gleam
5. sober	

Group 7	
1. 憎恨	2. 联络；联络员
3. 国会，代表大会	4. 摸得着的
5. 攀登；升高	6. 使入神
7. 安慰	
1. ascend	2. resents
3. liaison	4. console
5. tangible	

Group 8	
1. 记忆，回忆	2. 免疫力
3. 忍受；遵守	4. 接近
5. 外缘；外框	6. 累积的
7. 法令；裁定	
1. abide	2. proximity
3. immunity	4. cumulative
5. decree	

Group 9	
1. 静止不动的	2. 底线；起点
3. 怀疑态度	4. 召开；开会
5. 愤世嫉俗的	6. 性情
7. 蔓延；伸展	
1. temperament	2. stationary
3. baseline	4. convened
5. sprawled	

Group 10	
1. 鄙视，轻视	2. 琐碎的；次要的
3. 抚育	4. 推测的
5. 严峻的	6. 富有魅力的
7. 称赞	
1. glamorous	2. speculative
3. petty	4. dire
5. despised	

Word List 4

Group 1	
1. 类同	2. 极度痛苦
3. (达到)高潮	4. 怀旧；怀旧之情
5. 抢救；挽回	6. 危及
7. 先驱	
1. anguish	2. salvage
3. nostalgia	4. jeopardized
5. affinity	

Group 2	
1. 良性的	2. 预示
3. 羞耻；使…蒙受耻辱	4. 超越
5. 使迷惑	6. 暂时性的
7. 突出	
1. benign	2. herald
3. transcend	4. bewildered
5. disgraced	

Group 3	
1. 倾向于的	2. 便利设施
3. 情感的；深情的	4. 全部词汇
5. 翻新	6. 无数(的)，大量(的)
7. 困境	
1. plight	2. renovation
3. myriad	4. sentimental
5. amenity	

Group 4	
1. 加强	2. 混合物；企业集团
3. 轶事	4. 使混合
5. 陈词滥调	6. 多用途的；通用的
7. 普通的	
1. anecdotes	2. mingled
3. versatile	4. augmented
5. mundane	

Group 5	
1. 安慰剂；使人宽慰的东西	2. 使绝缘；使隔热
3. 危险；危害	4. 种族特点
5. 加重	6. 恳求；征集
7. 企业联合；财团；辛迪加	
1. peril	2. aggravate
3. soliciting	4. insulate
5. placebos	

Group 6	
1. 不实宣传，大肆宣传	2. 遗迹，废墟
3. 搅拌	4. 堵塞；阻碍
5. 理智的	6. 修辞的
7. 悲伤的，忧郁的	
1. cerebral	2. churn
3. melancholy	4. relics
5. rhetorical	

Group 7	
1. 回顾，回忆	2. 主角
3. 扣除	4. 不断骚扰；烦扰
5. 悲痛	6. 忠诚
7. 导航	
1. deduct	2. protagonist
3. allegiance	4. harassed
5. lamented	

Group 8	
1. 对称性	2. 悬荡
3. 吸收，使同化	4. 效仿，模仿
5. 极有趣的	6. 降落伞
7. 迎接，引座	
1. hilarious	2. ushered
3. dangling	4. emulate
5. assimilate	

Group 9	
1. 边缘	2. 吐露
3. 有冲突的	4. 无情的
5. 奢华的；丰富的	6. 先知
7. 有光泽的	
1. confided	2. lavish
3. relentless	4. prophet
5. brink	

Group 10	
1. 鲁莽的	2. 有争议的
3. 屈服	4. 使震惊
5. 惊人的	6. 鼓舞
7. 疾行，急速上升	
1. astounds	2. succumb
3. contentious	4. bolster
5. reckless	

Word List 5

Group 1	
1. 发怒；竖起(毛)	2. 古鲁(印度教精神导师)
3. 过于自负，虚荣心	4. 酸楚的
5. 阻碍	6. 子宫
7. 想象得到的	
1. womb	2. conceivable
3. vanity	4. bristle
5. impede	

Group 2	
1. 限制；监禁	2. 荒唐可笑的
3. 突发奇想	4. 设法促成
5. 精明的	6. 欺诈性的
7. 斜的，对角线的	
1. fraudulent	2. whim
3. confinement	4. diagonal
5. contrive	

Group 3	
1. 瑕疵；污染	2. 杂乱的东西
3. 整体的；全部的	4. 不同的
5. 调解；仲裁	6. 事后聪明
7. 迅速发展	
1. taint	2. holistic
3. disparate	4. hindsight
5. burgeon	

Group 4	
1. 预感；直觉	2. 昏暗的；严峻的
3. 大错	4. 不利的；有害的
5. 鄙视	6. 不祥的
7. (使)幻想破灭	
1. blunder	2. hunch
3. disdain	4. detrimental
5. disillusion	

Group 5	
1. 使陶醉	2. 看见
3. 阴沉的(情绪)	4. 一再反复的；无休止的
5. 胖乎乎的；使蓬松	6. 色彩
7. 患妄想症的；多疑的	
1. perpetual	2. paranoid
3. enchant	4. plump
5. dismal	

Group 6	
1. 将…谱成管弦乐曲	2. 宣布放弃；抛弃
3. 敬畏	4. 坚决的
5. 消遣	6. 漫画
7. 潜在的	
1. latent	2. renounce
3. pastime	4. revere
5. caricature	

Group 7	
1. 大草原，牧场	2. 经常光顾
3. 穿过	4. 预算的
5. 搜寻，觅食	6. 题写；雕刻
7. 壁画	
1. patronize	2. traverse
3. prairie	4. forage
5. budgetary	

Group 8	
1. 迸发	2. 抽打；彻底击败
3. 控告	4. 高耸的；高傲的
5. 名声显赫的；杰出的	6. 未察觉的
7. 到期未付的；逾期未还的	
1. indict	2. outburst
3. lofty	4. thrash
5. oblivious	

Group 9	
1. 校正	2. 耻辱
3. 非自愿的	4. 尴尬的处境
5. 衰落；枯萎	6. 成功的；狂欢的
7. 密谋	
1. wither	2. involuntary
3. rectify	4. conspire
5. triumphant	

Group 10	
1. 整修	2. 笨拙地做
3. 无益的	4. 使…偏斜；转移
5. 传授	6. 笨拙的；粗劣的
7. 变种的，突变的	
1. mutant	2. deflect
3. refurbish	4. futile
5. impart	

Word List 6

Group 1	
1. 热忱	2. 拉长，(使)延长
3. 枯燥的，沉闷的	4. 绕道
5. 错误的	6. 常识；技能
7. 吸引，诱惑	
1. fervor	2. erroneous
3. allure	4. detour
5. dreary	

Group 2	
1. 反响	2. 兼收并蓄的
3. 颠覆性的(人)	4. 哄劝
5. 慷慨	6. 减损
7. (穿上)服装	
1. coax	2. repercussion
3. subversive	4. eclectic
5. attire	

Group 3	
1. 同步	2. 挑衅的
3. 歇斯底里	4. 守卫部队
5. 驱逐	6. 热衷的；渴望的
7. 理解；逮捕	
1. defiant	2. apprehend
3. deport	4. synchronize
5. avid	

Group 4	
1. 首字母缩略词	2. (涂)清漆
3. 立法	4. 植物的，花的
5. 非凡的个人魅力	6. 奇迹般的
7. 包围，回避	
1. miraculous	2. circumvent
3. acronym	4. varnish
5. charisma	

Group 5	
1. 破坏，毁坏	2. 休息室
3. 懊悔	4. 冷笑；讥笑
5. 行为不良，违法犯罪	6. 辩护
7. 时代	
1. delinquency	2. vindicate
3. sneer	4. epoch
5. remorse	

Group 6	
1. 得体；礼仪	2. 上头的；浓烈的
3. 即兴表演	4. 悲悼；反对
5. 难以控制的	6. 惩戒
7. 笨重的	
1. cumbersome	2. reprimand
3. compulsive	4. decency
5. deplore	

Group 7	
1. 特权	2. 厌恶
3. 文盲；不识字的	4. 公正的；中立的
5. 艳丽的	6. 无瑕疵的
7. 迷惑	
1. impartial	2. prerogative
3. illiterate	4. aversion
5. captivate	

Group 8	
1. 独特的	2. 使…流产
3. 喘息；暂缓	4. 了不起的人或事
5. 责备；(使感到)耻辱	6. 吹嘘
7. 约会，会面	
1. brag	2. blockbuster
3. reproach	4. rendezvous
5. abort	

Group 9	
1. 挂毯	2. 容忍，忍受
3. 烹饪的	4. 把某人 / 某事物比作
5. 满不在乎的	6. 转向
7. 复兴	
1. tapestry	2. liken
3. complacent	4. brook
5. culinary	

Group 10	
1. 免责声明	2. 伪造(的)(东西)
3. 奸诈的，叛逆的	4. (帽)檐
5. 邋遢的；马虎的	6. 重读；加重音符号于
7. 方言(的)	
1. counterfeit	2. vernacular
3. treacherous	4. brim
5. sloppy	

Word List 7

Group 1	
1. 秘密的，偷偷摸摸的	2. 无缺点的
3. 僵局	4. 幻觉
5. 无经验的	6. 难点；关键
7. 以物换物	
1. crux	2. clandestine
3. impasse	4. fledgling
5. impeccable	

Group 2	
1. 枚举	2. 使疏远
3. 周围	4. 半透明的
5. 绝对的	6. (使)发酵
7. 轻蔑的	
1. categorical	2. enumerate
3. estrange	4. translucent
5. dismissive	

Group 3	
1. 使…脱轨	2. 使充满
3. 完整的，完美无缺的	4. 彻底了解；英寻
5. 礼节；规矩	6. 使合法；使合理
7. 呼气；终结；届期	
1. derail	2. fathom
3. consummate	4. expiration
5. imbue	

Group 4	
1. 虔诚的	2. 热情的
3. 冷淡	4. 恐惧症
5. 刺绣	6. 明显的
7. 之字形	
1. pious	2. palpable
3. embroidery	4. apathy
5. fervent	

Group 5	
1. 选举权	2. 错综复杂
3. 天资	4. 放掉…的气；瘪掉
5. 闲适恬静的	6. 不道德的，肆无忌惮的
7. 猖獗的，普遍的	
1. aptitude	2. intricacy
3. unscrupulous	4. suffrage
5. rife	

Group 6	
1. 节俭	2. 改善，减轻
3. 杀戮	4. 适宜的
5. 怪癖	6. 有传染性的
7. 贿赂	
1. bribery	2. ameliorate
3. contagious	4. quirks
5. expedient	

Group 7	
1. 明确坚决的	2. 热情洋溢的；过度的
3. 抑扬顿挫；终止	4. 多余的
5. (陷入)泥潭；困境	6. 轻浮的
7. 古老的	
1. emphatic	2. cadence
3. exuberant	4. frivolous
5. archaic	

Group 8	
1. 冷漠的	2. 对抗手段
3. 引逗	4. 教义；信条
5. 校正；调整	6. 爱好；倾向
7. 拥挤；拥塞	
1. penchant	2. calibrate
3. tantalize	4. dogma
5. aloof	

Group 9	
1. 退缩	2. 打赌
3. 筛子；过滤	4. 地形
5. 兜售	6. 冷酷无情的
7. 拆除；平息	
1. topography	2. recoiling
3. callous	4. sieve
5. peddle	

Group 10	
1. 享受；晒太阳	2. 事与愿违
3. 使人筋疲力尽的	4. 朴素的
5. 有礼貌的	6. 平等主义的
7. 警惕的	
1. backfire	2. austere
3. grueling	4. vigilant
5. bask	

Word List 8

Group 1	
1. 可理解的	2. 值得称赞的
3. 向…投掷	4. 谜语；难题
5. 预先阻止	6. 短暂的，转瞬即逝的
7. 隐秘的；难解的	
1. ephemeral	2. commendable
3. comprehensible	4. cryptic
5. forestall	

Group 2	
1. 缅怀往事	2. 偏僻地区
3. 含糊其辞的	4. 假装
5. 平庸的	6. 艰巨的；生硬的
7. 遗赠；传承	
1. banal	2. evasive
3. hinterland	4. reminisce
5. bequeath	

Group 3	
1. 无忧无虑的	2. 原型的
3. 欺骗(自己)	4. 写字潦草
5. 残留	6. 委婉语
7. 灵巧的	
1. euphemism	2. archetypal
3. vestige	4. delude
5. scrawl	

Group 4	
1. 比喻的	2. 不协调的，不一致的
3. 屈尊；表现出优越感	4. 使高兴
5. 无休止的	6. 合并
7. 赞美	
1. Figurative	2. incongruous
3. amalgamate	4. condescend
5. elate	

Group 5	
1. 约束	2. 保守的说法
3. 麻绳，细线；盘绕	4. 合并
5. 纪念(仪式)	6. 参与，分享
7. 典型的	
1. coalesce	2. twine
3. circumscribed	4. quintessential
5. understatement	

Group 6	
1. 呵斥	2. 嘲笑
3. 强烈的厌恶	4. 勤奋的
5. (为人处事)圆滑	6. 可口的
7. 贬低…的身份	
1. industrious	2. deride
3. demean	4. antipathy
5. palatable	

Group 7	
1. 偏执	2. 催化
3. 毫不含糊的	4. 歼灭；摧毁
5. 尖刻的	6. 持续不断的
7. 鉴赏家	
1. unequivocal	2. bigotry
3. connoisseur	4. annihilate
5. Incessant	

Group 8	
1. 平和的	2. 无能的；笨拙的
3. 预示	4. 地壳构造的
5. 假名；笔名	6. 内向的人
7. 喷嘴	
1. placid	2. tectonic
3. foreshadow	4. nozzle
5. inept	

Group 9	
1. 有教养的，体面的	2. 灾难
3. 发出轰鸣声	4. 把…并列
5. 打扰	6. 讽刺
7. 沉重的；繁重的	
1. sarcasm	2. pester
3. calamity	4. juxtapose/juxtaposed
5. genteel	

Group 10	
1. 喧嚣的；热烈的	2. 狡诈的
3. 在高处	4. 骚乱
5. (使)荒废	6. 告诫
7. 静谧	
1. commotion	2. devious
3. aloft	4. dilapidate
5. tumultuous	

Word List 9

Group 1	
1. 模棱两可的	2. 全能的
3. 刻板的	4. 不可撤回的
5. 地外的(生物)	6. 帝王的
7. 使不安	
1. extraterrestrial	2. perturbs
3. regal	4. irrevocable
5. formulaic	

Group 2	
1. 不足	2. 憎恶
3. 使动摇，使震荡	4. 简明的
5. 强烈的	6. 傲慢自大
7. 难以去除的	
1. succinct	2. hubris
3. oscillated	4. indelible
5. abhorred	

Group 3	
1. 删节	2. 口语的
3. 宣告…无效；废除	4. 错综复杂的
5. 用之不竭的	6. 性格外向的(人)
7. 动作机械的人	
1. colloquial	2. extrovert
3. inexhaustible	4. annulled
5. automaton	

Group 4	
1. 完全一致	2. 裂缝
3. 愉悦感官的	4. 无处不在的
5. 教导的	6. 短暂的
7. 渴望的；留恋的	
1. crevice	2. didactic
3. sensuous	4. transitory
5. wistful	

Group 5	
1. 蓄意破坏	2. 不停的
3. 吉利的	4. 易变的
5. 预告者	6. 对…施催眠术
7. 不透明；浑浊	
1. vandalized	2. hypnotize
3. fickle	4. auspicious
5. opacity	

Group 6	
1. 势不两立的；不相容的	2. 骇人听闻的；丑恶可耻的
3. 家庭女教师	4. (使)慌乱
5. 无法克服的；无法逾越的	6. 意味着；含言外之意
7. 违背	
1. irreconcilable	2. governess
3. fluster	4. insurmountable
5. flagrant	

Group 7	
1. 极坏的；极严重的	2. 得意扬扬
3. 敌意	4. 界限，边界
5. 劝诱	6. 使…年轻，有活力
7. 不可改变的	
1. gloat	2. enmity
3. cajoled	4. rejuvenate
5. immutable	

Group 8	
1. 蜿蜒的	2. 漫游者
3. 旋涡	4. 偷偷摸摸的
5. 镇静剂(的)	6. 演讲术
7. 减少	
1. serpentine	2. whirlpool
3. furtively	4. oratory
5. diminution	

Group 9	
1. 深不可测的	2. 恭敬的
3. 异教徒；离经叛道者	4. 有益的
5. 夸张	6. 枯燥的
7. 精明	
1. deferential	2. heretic
3. salutary	4. hyperbole
5. acumen	

Group 10	
1. 恶劣的	2. 淡色；些许味道
3. 极小的，无穷小的	4. 慎重的，细心的
5. 过高的	6. 鲜美多汁的；肉质的
7. 善于观察的；敏锐的	
1. abominable	2. infinitesimal
3. circumspect	4. Exorbitant
5. Succulent	

Word List 10

Group 1	
1. 冷漠的；单独的	2. 灾难性的
3. 看得清的	4. 杰出
5. 端庄稳重的	6. 古怪的
7. 抚慰	
1. cataclysmic	2. discernible
3. preeminence	4. Decorous
5. mollify	

Group 2	
1. 镇静的	2. 含硫磺的
3. 轻信的	4. 谬误的
5. 变迁	6. 满意的
7. 怨恨	
1. composed	2. credulous
3. fallacious	4. contented
5. rancor	

Group 3	
1. 宽敞的	2. 剽窃
3. 公正的，非利益相关的	4. 有远见的
5. 使入迷	6. 沙文主义
7. 区别	
1. commodious	2. plagiarized
3. disinterested	4. provident
5. discriminating	

Group 4	
1. 过于热情的	2. 瘦巴巴的
3. 探索	4. 非法性
5. 令人高兴的	6. 污染；玷污
7. 沉思的	
1. effusive	2. scrawny
3. exhilarating	4. defiled
5. pensive	

Group 5	
1. 密切的	2. 轻率无礼的
3. 隆重的	4. 临近；引起
5. 站得住脚的	6. 相反论点
7. 贪吃	
1. close-knit	2. flippant
3. ceremonious	4. drew on
5. tenable	

Group 6	
1. 乱开玩笑的	2. 令人恼怒的
3. 偷偷摸摸的	4. 祸根
5. 有吸引力的	6. 使不愉快地感到意外
7. 诱人的	
1. irksome	2. stealthy
3. bane	4. appealing
5. blindsided	

Group 7	
1. 无所不能的；全能的	2. 犹豫不决的
3. 令人扫兴的结尾	4. 贫穷的
5. 直的	6. 困惑
7. 陈旧的；过时的	
1. omnipotent	2. ambivalent
3. anticlimax	4. indigent
5. perplexities	

Group 8	
1. 头韵	2. 总计
3. 顶点	4. 清除，删除
5. 克制	6. 镇静
7. 难以形容的	
1. acme	2. expunge
3. forbore	4. equanimity
5. ineffable	

Group 9	
1. 抓紧	2. 教化
3. 轻率的	4. 有事业心的
5. 模仿	6. 轻松愉快的
7. 移情作用的；感情移入的	
1. edify	2. imprudent
3. enterprising	4. lighthearted
5. empathetic	

Group 10	
1. 偶然找到	2. 脾气坏的人
3. 对立的	4. 使谦卑，使出丑
5. 有效的	6. 势利的
7. 机敏的	
1. chanced on	2. adroit
3. efficacious	4. snobbish
5. abase	

提高级
Word List 1

Group 1	
1. 嘲弄	2. 控制杆；杠杆
3. 碰撞	4. 一批
5. 突袭	6. 合成的(物件)
7. 难民	
1. refugee	2. tease
3. raid	4. bump
5. synthetic	

Group 2	
1. 用拳猛击	2. 客厅；休息室
3. 管理	4. 母亲般的；母亲的
5. (打)结	6. 嗡嗡声；发出嗡嗡声
7. 定理	
1. supervise	2. knot
3. punch	4. buzz
5. maternal	

Group 3	
1. 诗	2. 浸；蘸
3. 不断的变动	4. 指示
5. 圆锥体	6. 肿瘤，肿块
7. 小教堂，小礼拜堂	
1. dip	2. verse
3. flux	4. tumor
5. denote	

Group 4	
1. (添加)说明/标题	2. 支架；行李架
3. 保证(给予)	4. 胆固醇
5. 螺钉	6. 宣布
7. 绞接(点)；粘接(点)	
1. proclaim	2. caption
3. rack	4. pledge
5. screw	

Group 5	
1. 标准	2. 少数；少数民族
3. 首次亮相	4. 氯化物
5. 耸肩	6. 医学的
7. 布道；宣传	
1. par	2. debut
3. minority	4. shrug
5. preach	

Group 6	
1. 语义的	2. 骤跌；倒下
3. 抗生素(的)	4. 象征(的)
5. 托盘	6. 跨步；进展
7. 蹒跚；跌跌撞撞地走	
1. token	2. stride
3. stumble	4. antibiotic
5. slump	

Group 7	
1. 分子的	2. 离子
3. 船队；车队	4. 男孩；哥们儿
5. 带子	6. 跌倒
7. 辅音的；一致的	
1. strap	2. tumble
3. consonant	4. fleet
5. molecular	

Group 8	
1. 名义上的	2. 子公司
3. 死亡数，死亡率	4. 界面
5. 盛宴	6. 数值的，数字的
7. 拍卖	
1. feast	2. auction
3. subsidiary	4. nominal
5. mortality	

Group 9	
1. 好斗的；激进分子	2. 无限
3. 叫喊	4. 拖延，推后
5. 经度的；纵向的	6. 恳求，请求
7. 争抢	
1. scramble	2. infinity
3. yell	4. plea
5. militant	

Group 10	
1. 批准	2. 厚板
3. 痣	4. 学位论文
5. 综合症状	6. 请愿书；请求
7. 符号	
1. dissertation	2. mole
3. sanction	4. notation
5. syndrome	

Word List 2

Group 1	
1. 沉思	2. 使负担，强迫
3. 宽敞的	4. (踩)踏板
5. 怜悯	6. 突然的一动
7. 捏，掐	
1. spacious	2. compassion
3. pinch	4. inflict
5. muse	

Group 2	
1. 赌场	2. 押韵，韵律
3. 围绕，包围	4. 受惠者
5. 以津贴补助	6. 动脉
7. 抵制	
1. artery	2. rhyme
3. boycott	4. encompass
5. subsidize	

Group 3	
1. 可行性	2. 野蛮的(人)
3. 鞭打	4. 想象
5. 配给券；优惠券	6. (被)豁免(的)
7. 主持；掌管	
1. savage	2. viability
3. exempt	4. lash
5. preside	

Group 4	
1. 疲惫的	2. 保释(金)
3. 钝的	4. 反抗
5. 劫数；毁灭	6. 保持
7. 滑动	
1. blunt	2. glide
3. weary	4. doom
5. revolt	

Group 5	
1. 使目眩	2. 声学的
3. 查明	4. 迄今
5. 平衡；镇定	6. 缰绳；牵制
7. 壁炉，炉栅	
1. dazzle	2. rein
3. acoustic	4. ascertain
5. poise	

Group 6	
1. 闪烁	2. 旋转
3. 夹紧	4. 批发(的/地)
5. 同狱犯人	6. 箔
7. 拉；拽	
1. glitters	2. wholesale
3. swirl	4. tug
5. foil	

Group 7	
1. 克制	2. 倾翻，颠覆
3. 边缘，界限	4. 开端
5. 晒黑(的皮肤)	6. 粉碎
7. 兜售	
1. verge	2. crumble
3. refrain	4. outset
5. overturn	

Group 8	
1. 占有(期)	2. 槽
3. 颤抖	4. 涂抹
5. 闪光	6. 严格的
7. 塞满	
1. tremble	2. rigorous
3. flare	4. Smear
5. cram	

Group 9	
1. 行走；踩，踏	2. 传教士(的)
3. 神学	4. 尉官
5. 夹子；衣服钩	6. 颤抖
7. 配音	
1. theology	2. dubbed
3. missionary	4. shiver
5. tread	

Group 10	
1. 道德，士气	2. 胰岛素
3. 墓地	4. 船的，海军的
5. 麻烦事，讨厌的人	6. 咬碎，压碎
7. 斜面	
1. morale	2. nuisance
3. naval	4. ramp
5. crunch	

Word List 3

Group 1	
1. 驱逐	2. 明显的
3. 专政	4. 突出的，显著的
5. 假定	6. 使成流线型
7. 矮而宽的	
1. squat	2. salient
3. presumption	4. oust
5. conspicuous	

Group 2	
1. 洒；撒	2. 颤抖；战栗
3. 大修	4. 卫生
5. 繁茂的，茂盛的	6. 快照
7. 君主	
1. shudder	2. lush
3. sprinkle	4. monarch
5. Hygiene	

Group 3	
1. 渴望	2. (发出)隆隆声
3. 恶棍	4. 绷带
5. 传播	6. 沼泽
7. 行业的；业务的	
1. disseminate	2. vocational
3. rumble	4. yearn
5. villain	

Group 4	
1. 网状物	2. 轻声笑
3. 欺骗	4. 投掷
5. 教皇	6. 用魔术变出
7. 柔软的，软弱的	
1. limp	2. conjure
3. Pope	4. hurl
5. chuckle	

Group 5	
1. 废除	2. 酸橙；石灰
3. 避开，移开	4. 折磨
5. (到达)顶点	6. 统一体
7. 行话	
1. repeal	2. avert
3. crest	4. torment
5. jargon	

Group 6	
1. 凹处；幽深处	2. 普遍的
3. 交往，交流	4. 渴望，贪求
5. 暗杀	6. 不停摆弄
7. 破坏；玷污	
1. pervasive	2. assassinate
3. intercourse	4. marred
5. recesses	

Group 7	
1. 闲逛	2. 所有者
3. 日元	4. 光滑的
5. 高兴	6. 小跑
7. 人类学家	
1. proprietor	2. slick
3. trot	4. ramble
5. rejoice	

Group 8	
1. 固定装置	2. 终有一死的；不免一死的
3. 弯曲	4. 抱怨
5. 发狂似的；狂乱的	6. 投掷
7. 堡垒	
1. grumble	2. frantic
3. flex	4. mortal
5. sling	

Group 9	
1. 嚎叫；哀号	2. 肠
3. 呕吐(物)	4. 加剧，恶化
5. 如画的；生动的	6. 眨眼
7. 脸红	
1. vomit	2. howl
3. exacerbate	4. wink
5. blush	

Group 10	
1. (切成)碎片	2. (发出)嘶嘶声
3. 粗糙的	4. 算术(的)
5. 手镯，手链	6. 剪(羊毛)
7. 习惯上的	
1. arithmetic	2. rugged
3. customary	4. shred
5. shear	

Word List 4

Group 1	
1. 中子	2. 尖叫，尖声
3. 涉水；费力前行	4. 盛怒
5. (使)倾斜	6. 洗涤剂
7. 纠正	
1. shriek	2. wade
3. detergent	4. wrath
5. slant	

Group 2	
1. 雾	2. 气氛；气场
3. 有用	4. 躲避
5. 爱国者	6. 觊觎
7. 放弃	
1. elude	2. haze
3. avail	4. covet
5. aura	

Group 3	
1. 哀号；恸哭	2. 一致，同意
3. 俯身	4. 飞地
5. 谦逊	6. 怪异的
7. 深红色的；红衣主教	
1. concur	2. wail
3. stoop	4. cardinal
5. humility	

Group 4	
1. 甲烷	2. 代用品，替代物
3. 完全的(地)	4. 驱散
5. 缺乏	6. 过度的
7. 放逐	
1. undue	2. dispel
3. downright	4. surrogate
5. banish	

Group 5	
1. 陷阱；隐患	2. 小溪
3. 色情的	4. 蓄意破坏
5. 心灵，精神	6. 反的；相反的事物
7. 使发痒	
1. sabotage	2. inverse
3. pitfall	4. psyche
5. tickle	

Group 6	
1. 猩红色的	2. 狂热的
3. 猖獗的	4. 迂回的
5. 虚张声势	6. 使苦恼
7. 调色板	
1. fanatic	2. bluff
3. ail	4. scarlet
5. rampant	

Group 7	
1. 生锈的	2. 倒钩；倒刺
3. 焚香(时的烟)	4. 重击
5. 孵化	6. 拍翅膀
7. 有弹性的	
1. rusty	2. resilient
3. incubate	4. whack
5. incense	

Group 8	
1. 穿衣服的	2. 国歌；颂歌
3. 回旋	4. 逐渐减少
5. 市民；市政当局	6. 矮胖的
7. 同义的	
1. whirl	2. stout
3. taper	4. clad
5. anthem	

Group 9	
1. 咕哝	2. 触角
3. 跳蚤	4. 潦草地写字；涂鸦
5. 峡谷	6. 违法的
7. (打成)浆	
1. antenna	2. illicit
3. mumble	4. scribble
5. gorge	

Group 10	
1. 降级	2. 渗入
3. 破裂	4. (毛发)油亮的
5. 指责	6. 新陈代谢的
7. 慌张，骚动	
1. infiltrate	2. rupture
3. flurry	4. relegate
5. rebuke	

Word List 5

Group 1	
1. 抵消	2. 账本
3. 疯狂的，愚蠢的	4. 抚弄，弄皱
5. 可怕的	6. 迫使
7. 唾液	
1. ruffled	2. counteract
3. obligates	4. saliva
5. lunatic	

Group 2	
1. 报复	2. 镀金，修饰
3. 放松	4. 衰退
5. 友爱	6. 壁画
7. 离奇的	
1. uncanny	2. gild
3. unwind	4. fraternity
5. ebb	

Group 3	
1. 凝块	2. 罚金
3. 闪光	4. 烧焦
5. 父系的	6. 色彩，染色
7. 赎金	
1. scorch	2. glistens
3. forfeit	4. clot
5. tint	

Group 4	
1. 友好	2. 间谍活动
3. 激怒	4. 怒气
5. 流出，渗出	6. 紧握
7. 踩踏	
1. rapport	2. espionage
3. trample	4. exasperate
5. tantrum	

Group 5	
1. 巨大的	2. 协会
3. 刺，戳	4. 天资
5. 琐事	6. 极丑的
7. 毛虫	
1. grotesque	2. monstrous
3. flair	4. prick
5. caterpillar	

Group 6	
1. 亲切的，友善的	2. 篡改，干预
3. 灶台，壁炉	4. 凶猛的
5. 痴迷	6. 延长
7. 保护，保存	
1. amiable	2. tamper
3. protract	4. fixation
5. ferocious	

Group 7	
1. 没收	2. 使消散
3. 蜂巢	4. (发出)噼啪声
5. 注入，灌输	6. 一大群
7. 恶作剧	
1. mischief	2. confiscate
3. hive	4. crackle
5. horde	

Group 8	
1. 圆形隆起物	2. 推论
3. 背叛	4. (陷入)僵局
5. 轰炸，炮击	6. 迟缓的
7. 流逝	
1. sluggish	2. treason
3. elapse	4. corollary
5. hump	

Group 9	
1. 长期争执	2. 开端
3. 抽动，颤动	4. 一大群
5. 宣传	6. 家谱，血统
7. 古色古香的，老派的	
1. promulgate	2. pedigree
3. feud	4. prelude
5. throb	

Group 10	
1. 关节	2. 迷信
3. 散播	4. 麻醉剂
5. 瞬间的，即刻的	6. 狼吞虎咽
7. 隔离	
1. strew	2. gulp
3. instantaneous	4. knuckle
5. seclude	

Word List 6

Group 1	
1. 抚慰，平息	2. 心烦意乱的
3. 多孔的	4. 瞌睡
5. 人造黄油	6. 哑剧
7. 小步疾走	
1. appease	2. scuttle
3. mime	4. distraught
5. doze	

Group 2	
1. 超过	2. (做)鬼脸
3. 乘人之危者	4. 夜间的
5. 全景	6. 监管人
7. 纵容	
1. pamper	2. outstrip
3. custodian	4. vulture
5. nocturnal	

Group 3	
1. 涉猎	2. 成熟的，老练的
3. 喋喋不休	4. 翻找
5. 运输	6. 叠加，附加
7. 放大	
1. rummage	2. conveyance
3. babble	4. superimpose
5. magnification	

Group 4	
1. 干涉	2. 恢复
3. 客栈，小酒馆	4. 包围，围攻
5. 再装满	6. 不活动的
7. 渗出；散发	
1. rehabilitate	2. tavern
3. exude	4. meddle
5. besiege	

Group 5	
1. 烧灼	2. 难以置信的
3. 沉重缓慢地走	4. 景色
5. 宽恕	6. (感到)刺痛
7. 挥霍	
1. condone	2. inconceivable
3. tingle	4. squander
5. trudge	

Group 6	
1. 取代	2. 惩罚
3. 尖声(嘲笑)	4. 畏缩
5. 闪光	6. 序曲；开端
7. 公共卫生	
1. sanitation	2. glimmer
3. cringe	4. overture
5. retribution	

Group 7	
1. 捐助人	2. 挖苦的，讽刺的
3. 喧闹，混乱	4. 唆使，煽动
5. 清算	6. 喧闹的
7. 回响，鸣响	
1. liquidation	2. wry
3. uproar	4. raucous
5. instigate	

Group 8	
1. 加前缀；置于…之前	2. 精神正常
3. 弹弓；飞机弹射器	4. 斜体字(的)
5. 突然转向	6. 正直的
7. 避免	
1. eschew	2. prefixed
3. swerve	4. catapult
5. italic	

Group 9	
1. 循环的，周期的	2. 摄入
3. 乳房，胸部	4. 巨蛇
5. 冥想	6. 敌意
7. 顶点	
1. vertex	2. ingest
3. bosom	4. serpent
5. animosity	

Group 10	
1. 阐明	2. 鼓励；使浮起
3. 收回，撤回	4. 憎恶
5. 支撑	6. 瞪视
7. 颂扬	
1. exalt	2. buoy
3. elucidate	4. detest
5. retract	

Word List 7

Group 1	
1. 演出团	2. 同胞；同国人
3. 给…消毒	4. 使有活力
5. 水沟	6. 林荫大道
7. 给…作注释	
1. troupe	2. sterilize
3. compatriot	4. invigorate
5. annotate	

Group 2	
1. 讨价还价	2. 斑点
3. 争吵	4. 美甲
5. 扎紧	6. 迫使
7. 深长的切口	
1. trussed	2. manicure
3. bicker	4. gash
5. impelled	

Group 3	
1. 无法穿透的	2. 公开谴责
3. 崩溃，暴跌	4. 恶作剧
5. 附加	6. 朝臣
7. 无比的	
1. courtier	2. prank
3. unparalleled	4. meltdown
5. impenetrable	

Group 4	
1. 夸张的	2. 露水
3. 独裁的	4. 放弃
5. 技巧，策略	6. (使)圣化
7. 切碎	
1. consecrate	2. hashed
3. melodramatic	4. forsake
5. dew	

Group 5	
1. 拒绝	2. 保险柜，金库
3. 洪亮的	4. 颂扬
5. 无畏的	6. 整理，校对
8. (使)后倾	
1. resonant	2. collated
3. intrepid	4. rebuff
5. coffer	

Group 6	
1. 久坐的	2. 明智的
3. 使卷入	4. (使)惊呆，(使)石化
5. 挥击	6. 井井有条的
7. 刺耳的	
1. swipe	2. strident
3. embroil	4. judicious
5. methodical	

Group 7	
1. 挑剔的	2. 坚决的
3. 狡猾的	4. 不一致
5. 畏缩	6. 真菌的
7. 狼吞虎咽	
1. fussy	2. resolute
3. quailed	4. gobble
5. fungal	

Group 8	
1. 结巴	2. 降临
3. 撤销	4. 顺从的
5. 跛行	6. 假的
7. 无能的	
1. fictitious	2. impotent
3. rescind	4. befall
5. stutter	

Group 9	
1. 使适应	2. 倒退
3. 大洞穴	4. 先锋
5. (用)锄头(锄地)	6. 早于
7. (起)泡沫	
1. predate	2. cavern
3. regress	4. vanguard
5. froths	

Group 10	
1. 忏悔	2. 匆忙的
3. 哄骗	4. 碱性的
5. 毗邻的	6. 难控制的
7. 垂头丧气	
1. unruly	2. hoaxed
3. contiguous	4. repent
5. cursory	

Word List 8

Group 1	
1. 沙哑的	2. 流苏
3. 抽吸	4. 精致的，小巧玲珑的
5. 发狂的	6. 灌输
7. (人群等)蜂拥	
1. hoarse	2. suction
3. dainty	4. impregnated
5. stampede	

Group 2	
1. 狂喜	2. 砍掉…的头
3. 爱交际的	4. 揭穿
5. 昏昏欲睡的	6. 极恶的
7. 点燃	
1. debunk	2. gregarious
3. rapture	4. kindle
5. decapitate	

Group 3	
1. 温顺的	2. 汗水
3. 缄默的	4. 安抚
5. 同盟的	6. 克服
7. 刚开始的	
1. reticent	2. docile
3. confederate	4. incipient
5. perspiration	

Group 4	
1. 敷衍的	2. 取消抵押品赎回权
3. 纵容的	4. 一缕
5. 不情愿的	6. 折磨，使痛苦
7. 不溶的	
1. tendrils	2. indulgent
3. loath	4. perfunctory
5. foreclose	

Group 5	
1. 精明的	2. 柔软的
3. 码头	4. 暗示
5. 扰乱	6. 陡峭的
7. 祖先，创始人	
1. derange	2. supple
3. precipitous	4. insinuate
5. wharf	

Group 6	
1. 供应者	2. 无法改变的
3. 隐居者	4. 吉祥物
5. 不清楚的	6. 影射
7. 狂热的	
1. innuendo	2. zealous
3. recluse	4. mascot
5. indistinct	

Group 7	
1. 轻率	2. 对立面
3. 花蜜	4. 兴奋
5. 吸入	6. 易受骗的
7. 倾泻	
1. indiscretion	2. antithesis
3. zest	4. nectar
5. inhalation	

Group 8	
1. 隐士	2. 避免，消除
3. 虚伪的	4. 使干枯
5. 照亮	6. 使惊呆
7. 勇敢的	
1. disingenuous	2. irradiate
3. hermit	4. valiant
5. parches	

Group 9	
1. 鬼鬼祟祟的；卑鄙的	2. 推进
3. 熄灭	4. 扭打，争执
5. 征服，击败	6. 充满
7. 节俭的	
1. quench	2. vanquish
3. suffuse	4. sneaky
5. tussle	

Group 10	
1. 洗劫	2. 通风
3. 反省的	4. 丰满的
5. 迷恋	6. 球状物
7. 简洁的	
1. ransacked	2. orbs
3. ventilate	4. fetish
5. chubby	

Word List 9

Group 1	
1. 端庄娴静的	2. 不知疲倦的
3. 信件	4. 难以捉摸的
5. 使起(涟漪)	6. 雕刻
7. 引爆；爆炸	
1. incised	2. detonations
3. indefatigable	4. demure
5. inscrutable	

Group 2	
1. 波动	2. 应受指责的
3. 换毛；换羽	4. 六边形的
5. 不寻常的，非传统的	6. 棘齿条
7. 炽烈的；灼热的	
1. reprehensible	2. molt
3. offbeat	4. undulation
5. torpid	

Group 3	
1. 滑行；凭惯性前进	2. 投枪；标枪
3. 乏味(的)	4. 不友好的；不利的
5. 把…分为两部分	6. 回扣
7. 象形文字(的)	
1. inimical	2. freewheel
3. humdrum	4. bisected
5. kickbacks	

Group 4	
1. 使折射	2. 崇敬
3. [俄罗斯的]宇航员	4. 蓬松卷曲的毛发；绒毛
5. 食肉的；食虫的	6. 无赖
7. 臆想的事	
1. refract	2. figment
3. scoundrel	4. venerated
5. carnivorous	

Group 5	
1. 涂鸦	2. 唐吉诃德式的；不切实际的
3. 恳求	4. 贪吃的，渴求的
5. 分裂	6. 质朴；天真
7. 不知情的	
1. quixotic	2. doodles
3. voracious	4. entreating
5. unwitting	

Group 6	
1. 易弯的	2. 学究式的；卖弄学问的
3. 阴郁的	4. 妨碍
5. 使成斑驳；使多样化	6. 猩猩
7. 持续的；不懈的	
1. pedantic	2. morose
3. unremitting	4. encumbered
5. pliable	

Group 7	
1. 鹅叫声；喇叭声	2. 和谐
3. 摇篮曲	4. 使复苏
5. 诈骗	6. 叶绿素
7. 老生常谈的	
1. resuscitate	2. concord
3. lullaby	4. trite
5. swindled	

Group 8	
1. 宏伟的，壮丽的	2. 快乐的
3. 坚忍的人；寡欲的人	4. 误解
5. 热情洋溢的	6. 展开
7. 否认	
1. disavowed	2. jovial
3. ebullient	4. misconstrued
5. palatial	

Group 9	
1. 预谋	2. 懒洋洋地倚靠
3. 欢乐；欢笑	4. 正直
5. 煽动者	6. 长方形(的)
7. 偶然的	
1. premeditate	2. merriment
3. demagogue	4. fortuitous
5. lolling	

Group 10	
1. (发出)叮当声	2. 敲诈；侵占
3. 分贝；响度	4. 击退
5. 嬉戏	6. 无精打采的
7. 卸除…的锋头	
1. listless	2. extorting
3. repulsed	4. tinkled
5. frolic	

Word List 10

Group 1	
1. 樟脑	2. 乘火车
3. 犹豫	4. 道德败坏；士气消沉
5. 充分满足	6. 相异；不同
7. 宿命论的	
1. otherness	2. satiate
3. demoralization	4. fatalistic
5. vacillate	

Group 2	
1. 正面，门面	2. 帽子戏法
3. (智力上)超过；胜过	4. 累积；混乱
5. 喋喋不休的	6. 羞怯的
7. 吸引；诱骗	
1. beguile	2. pileup
3. bashful	4. garrulous
5. outsmarts/outsmarted	

Group 3	
1. 厌恶人类者	2. 表明；宣言
3. 先生(西班牙语中一种男性称呼)	4. 健谈的
5. 使重新开始	6. (使变得)柔软的
7. 推进物	
1. recommence	2. loquacious
3. limber	4. enunciate
5. misanthrope	

Group 4	
1. 啰嗦的	2. 业余爱好
3. 剪报	4. 流行的；时尚的
5. 真菌；霉菌	6. 溶解
7. (使用)水槽(引水)	
1. faddish	2. verbose
3. avocation	4. fungi
5. dissolved	

Group 5	
1. 残遗物	2. 开动；促使
3. 谴责；抨击	4. 使困窘；使羞愧
5. 放荡的	6. 责备；指责
7. 不能克服的	
1. reproved	2. insuperable
3. dissolute	4. abashed
5. denunciate	

Group 6	
1. 麻木的	2. 等边的
3. 曙光	4. 削减；减少
5. 逆时针方向的	6. 健谈者
7. 爬行的	
1. torpid	2. aurora
3. raconteur	4. cut back
5. creeping	

Group 7	
1. 取消	2. 肥沃的，多产的
3. 慷慨的	4. 饲养；繁殖
5. 即兴表演	6. 拟声法
7. 平息；消散	
1. munificent	2. countermanded
3. fecund	4. extemporize
5. blow over	

Group 8	
1. 无法挽回的	2. 虎头蛇尾的人；半途而废者
3. 强求	4. 开始的；早期的
5. 摘要；总结	6. 抛物线
7. 使无力	
1. quitter	2. inchoate
3. irretrievable	4. enervated
5. importunity	

Group 9	
1. 使沮丧，使灰心	2. 恶意
3. 讽刺的	4. 吹捧；奉为名人
5. 子女的	6. 卸载；下船
7. 炽热的；发光；发热	
1. lionized	2. satiric
3. filial	4. dejects
5. glowing	

Group 10	
1. 平静的；平稳的	2. 厌倦；无聊
3. 傲慢；无礼	4. 端正
5. 兴奋的；冒泡的	6. 贪婪；贪心
7. 优柔寡断的	
1. insolence	2. effervescent
3. halcyon	4. cupidity
5. irresolute	

全能级
Word List 1

Group 1	
1. 风帽，兜帽	2. 船桅
3. 荚果	4. 圣所；避难所
5. 黄铜	6. 擦洗
7. 强烈反对	
1. scrubbed	2. hood
3. brass	4. sanctuary
5. backlash	

Group 2	
1. 类，种，属	2. 下水道
3. 绝对真理	4. 主音(的)
5. 葡萄糖	6. 仓库；车库
7. 取决于	
1. sewer	2. hinge
3. depot	4. gospel
5. genus	

Group 3	
1. 覆盖物	2. 木板；铺木板
3. 额头，眉毛	4. 心脏(病)的
5. 抢走，夺走	6. 铺位
7. 一窝	
1. brood	2. brow
3. snatched	4. mantle
5. cardiac	

Group 4	
1. 女管事	2. 哮喘
3. 竹茎，藤条	4. 衣柜；全部衣物
5. 管道	6. 切；割
7. 长笛	
1. canes	2. wardrobe
3. duct	4. slit
5. mistress	

Group 5	
1. 屈膝；蜷缩	2. 牛犊
3. 丰富	4. 压扁；挤压
5. 畜牧的	6. 叶，枝叶
7. 接种	
1. crouched	2. squashing
3. vaccinations	4. pastoral
5. amplitude	

Group 6	
1. 稀释，削弱	2. 鼓起
3. 卵石，大圆石	4. 暴行；残暴
5. 可耻的，无法容忍的	6. 家系，血统
7. 男高音	
1. dilute	2. atrocity
3. bulged	4. outrageous
5. lineage	

Group 7	
1. 搭扣，扣紧	2. 严格的
3. (全部)可表演项目	4. 吹小号；宣扬
5. 弹道；轨道	6. 蟋蟀
7. 钾	
1. trumpet/trumpeted	2. trajectory
3. repertoire	4. buckled
5. stringent	

Group 8	
1. 行家，有学问的人	2. 散发；发出
3. 污水	4. 胡须；额毛
5. 民谣	6. 病毒性的
7. 咆哮	
1. viral	2. pundits
3. raving	4. emanating
5. ballads	

Group 9	
1. 兽穴；窝点	2. 通灵的(人)
3. 契约	4. 唯恐；以免
5. 家禽(肉)	6. 加固；使做好准备
7. 障碍	
1. braced	2. hurdle
3. covenant	4. lest
5. den	

Group 10	
1. 朋友，支持者；一群人	2. 屠夫；屠宰
3. 哀悼；表示遗憾	4. 猛拍；撞击(声)
5. 拉；拖	6. 线缝；接缝
7. 糕点	
1. smack	2. mourns
3. seams	4. cohorts
5. heaved/heaves	

Word List 2

Group 1

1. 突然倾斜；突然改变	2. 野猪；公猪
3. 卧铺	4. 绞碎；碎肉
5. 糖浆	6. 合乎良心的
7. 盥洗室；抽水马桶	
1. minced	2. conscientious
3. lurched	4. lavatory
5. berth	

Group 2

1. 选集	2. 水貂；貂皮大衣
3. 同情，共鸣	4. 骑，跨坐
5. 不正当的，堕落的	6. 胡乱堆放；(使)混乱
7. 附属建筑物	
1. anthologies	2. sympathize
3. straddled	4. perverse
5. jumble	

Group 3

1. (用)曲柄(启动)	2. 游说
3. 阴暗的	4. 鲤鱼
5. 移居国外的；侨民	6. 躯干
7. 视网膜	
1. torso	2. expatriate
3. murky	4. cranked
5. canvassed	

Group 4

1. 面容；容许	2. 使某人戒掉
3. 大风	4. 幽灵；恐惧
5. 举(抬、持)…的人	6. 此后
7. 抛接，玩杂耍	
1. wean	2. bearer
3. countenanced	4. henceforth
5. specter	

Group 5

1. 握紧；抱紧	2. 嗥叫；厉声说
3. 疾驰	4. 对…感到懊悔，悲叹
5. 放射性坠尘；污染性坠尘	6. 扭；拽；拧
7. 破败的；荒废的	
1. clasped	2. rued
3. snarling	4. gallop
5. derelict	

Group 6

1. 喷出；(发出)哼声	2. 迫害
3. 门闩；弹簧锁	4. 反驳，回嘴
5. 洗礼	6. 下垂，下陷
7. 抽搐	
1. latch	2. retort
3. persecution	4. sagged
5. baptisms	

Group 7

1. 挣扎，折腾	2. 不稳定的；古怪的
3. 树丛，小树林	4. 软木；(用)软木塞(塞住)
5. 煨炖	6. 少女
7. 肠道的	
1. simmering	2. cork
3. floundering	4. erratic
5. maidens	

Group 8

1. 猛拉	2. [地理]岩脊
3. 嘎吱作响	4. 移植；贪污
5. [化学]氯	6. 摸索，探索
7. (使成为)糊状物	
1. graft	2. yanked
3. grope	4. ledges
5. Mashed	

Group 9

1. 光谱的	2. 辛勤工作
3. 授…以圣职	4. 鳕鱼
5. 平等	6. 检验，化验
7. 围裙	
1. toil/toiled	2. spectral
3. parity	4. ordained
5. assayed	

Group 10

1. 大男子气的	2. 摧毁，破坏，劫掠
3. 惯例，法令	4. 大麦
5. 护林员	6. (把…装)箱
7. 生面团	
1. macho	2. ravaged
3. rangers	4. ordiance
5. crated	

Word List 3

Group 1	
1. 移走；逐出	2. 白桦树；桦木
3. 令人反感的；难闻的	4. 水坑
5. 摇晃	6. 推断，推测
7. (使)改变主意	
1. obnoxious	2. extrapolate
3. wobbles	4. dislodge
5. budge	

Group 2	
1. 歪曲真相，掩饰	2. 唯利是图的；贪财的
3. 原始的	4. 把手
5. 拥护者	6. 困扰
7. 树脂	
1. mercenary	2. primordial
3. besetting	4. exponent
5. belies/belied	

Group 3	
1. 基因型	2. 抗氧化剂，硬化防止剂
3. 十四行诗	4. 便携式摄像机
5. 地震的	6. 猛烈攻击，突击
7. 斗殴；争吵	
1. brawling	2. onslaught
3. sonnets	4. antioxidants
5. seismic	

Group 4	
1. 依法驱逐	2. 喷射；喷出
3. 幼兽	4. 精明的，聪慧的
5. (发出)咝咝声	6. 虚假的，伪造的
7. 骨干队伍	
1. astute	2. evict
3. squirt	4. spurious
5. cadres	

Group 5	
1. 闪光	2. 过多
3. 斜视	4. 隐喻的
5. 劈开；坚持	6. (对…执行)缓刑
7. 调制；编造	
1. glinting	2. metaphorical
3. cleaves/clove	4. concoct
5. plethora	

Group 6	
1. 无政府主义者 (的)	2. 妙语；俏皮话
3. 窑	4. (分套)公寓楼
5. 圆周，周围	6. 传说，典故
7. (剧团/演员)所有可以表演的曲目	
1. quip	2. lore
3. circumference	4. anarchists
5. condos	

Group 7	
1. 寓言故事	2. 大摇大摆，傲慢地走路
3. 得意地笑	4. 突出，伸出
5. 出现	6. 奢华的
7. 跑步机	
1. protruding	2. swaggered
3. smirked	4. transpired
5. sumptuous	

Group 8	
1. [矿]石英	2. 棚屋
3. (使用)蜡笔(作画)	4. 米色(的)，淡棕色(的)
5. 肾上腺素	6. 初期的，开始形成的，新兴的
7. 婴儿床	
1. quartz	2. crayons
3. shacks	4. nascent
5. beige	

Group 9	
1. [化学]镁	2. 畏缩，回避
3. 瓶，长颈瓶	4. 海军上将，舰队司令
5. 浅滩	6. 聚光灯
7. 坚定分子；坚定的	
1. limelight	2. flask
3. admiral	4. stalwart
5. balk	

Group 10	
1. 沉重缓慢地行走	2. 细丝
3. 支持	4. 藏匿；藏匿物
5. 不当的行为	6. 迂回曲折
7. 戒绝	
1. plodded	2. buttress
3. meander	4. abstaining
5. stashed	

Word List 4

Group 1	
1. 针叶树	2. 隼；猎鹰
3. 水仙花	4. (鸭子发出)嘎嘎声
5. 三叶草	6. 与世隔绝的；岛屿的
7. 湿漉漉的	
1. falcons	2. soggy
3. insular	4. clover
5. conifers	

Group 2	
1. 赞扬，荣誉	2. 月桂树
3. 暴雨，洪水	4. 深坑；裂缝；断层
5. [化]磷	6. 头朝前的(地)
7. 高声鸣响；(使发出)刺耳的声音	
1. deluge	2. accolades
3. headlong	4. blared
5. chasm	

Group 3	
1. 安抚，抚慰	2. 各式各样的
3. 引起；成为…之父	4. 空运
5. 相称的，相当的	6. [化]钴
7. 挡风玻璃	
1. windshields	2. airlift
3. commensurate	4. placate
5. begetting	

Group 4	
1. 丛林狼，草原狼	2. [音乐]对位法；对应物
3. 征兆；预兆	4. 家宅
5. 友善的；真诚的；亲切的	6. 挑剔，发牢骚
7. 规劝，敦促	
1. genial	2. quibbles
3. counterpoint	4. omen
5. exhorts	

Group 5	
1. 盛气凌人的，自以为是的	2. 大声咀嚼
3. 和平主义者(的)	4. (尤指某职业特有的)服装
5. 松饼	6. 火炉围栏
7. [音]奏鸣曲	
1. sonatas	2. pacifists
3. munched	4. garbs
5. brash	

Group 6	
1. 眩晕的	2. 虚张声势；逞能
3. 怂恿；煽动；迎合	4. 暗中为害的；潜在的
5. 泄露	6. 早熟的，智慧超前的
7. 神性；神	
1. bravado	2. insidioius
3. pandering	4. precocious
5. divulge	

Group 7	
1. 惊恐；焦虑，不安	2. 食品储藏室
3. 谚语的	4. 毁灭性的，世界末日的
5. 同志情谊，友情	6. 藐视，轻视(法律等)
7. 偷听	
1. eavesdrop	2. trepidation
3. flouting	4. apocalytic
5. camaraderie	

Group 8	
1. 灾难；祸害	2. 枯萎，凋谢
3. 荒谬的	4. 鱿鱼
5. 卑劣的；可耻的	6. 骇人的
7. 优势，大多数	
1. preponderance	2. sordid
3. preposterous	4. wilt
5. scourge	

Group 9	
1. 燧石；打火石	2. [化]阳离子
3. 奇思妙想，怪异多变	4. 稍稍卷曲的
5. 大批毁灭	6. 突然说出
7. 不忠(行为)	
1. blurt	2. wavy
3. infidelity	4. decimated
5. vagaries	

Group 10	
1. 原始的；根本的	2. 呜咽，啜泣
3. [法]废除，使无效	4. 不服从命令的(人)；顽抗的(人)
5. 敏捷的，机智的	6. 有毒的，有害的
7. 摈弃，傲慢地回绝	
1. recalcitrant	2. spurned
3. quash	4. primal
5. noxious	

Word List 5

Group 1	
1. 引起嫉妒的	2. 黑手党
3. 温顺的	4. 特异景象；幽灵
5. 混杂的	6. 主显节
7. 反责	
1. motley	2. meek
3. recrimination	4. enviable
5. mafia	

Group 2	
1. 孤独的，凄凉的	2. 心脏病学
3. 矮壮的	4. 使脱离
5. 斑点；使呈杂色	6. 烧杯；大口杯
7. 微观世界，小宇宙	
1. microcosm	2. extricate
3. forlorn	4. mottle
5. stocky	

Group 3	
1. (提出)异议	2. 乳液
3. 亵渎的	4. 留声机
5. 丁香花；紫色(的)	6. [音乐]渐强
7. 跨着，叉开	
1. phonograph	2. astride
3. demur	4. profane
5. crescendo	

Group 4	
1. 颂诗	2. 多边形
3. 超凡的；优雅的	4. 分配
5. 当当响	6. 使分层
7. 粘稠的	
1. polygon	2. apportioned
3. clanged	4. ethereal
5. stratified	

Group 5	
1. 藏匿	2. 揉；按摩
3. 默许	4. 门卫
5. [几何]同心的	6. 无关的
7. 格言	
1. extraneous	2. sequestered
3. acquiesced	4. knead
5. bouncer	

Group 6	
1. 渐增；堆积物	2. 尖利的碎片
3. 过时的	4. 鸵鸟
5. 发出咝咝声	6. 箭头
7. 痴迷	
1. fizzled	2. infatuation
3. shard	4. accretion
5. anachronistic	

Group 7	
1. 苦修	2. 转世化身；转世说
3. 桶	4. 忸怩的
5. 微不足道的	6. 祖先，祖宗
7. 有害的	
1. deleterious	2. reincarnation
3. paltry	4. penance
5. coy	

Group 8	
1. 山谷	2. 刺穿
3. 精瘦的	4. 充满的
5. 传送者，传送带	6. 缝合(处)
7. 淡紫色(的)	
1. perforated	2. conveyor
3. wiry	4. replete
5. mauve	

Group 9	
1. 警戒	2. 使正式就职
3. 亵渎神灵	4. 闲逛
5. 颂词	6. 冻原
7. 坚持；砍，劈	
1. sentineled	2. hewed/hew
3. loitering	4. inducted
5. blasphemy	

Group 10	
1. 变形	2. 萎缩；衰退
3. 可塑的	4. (发出)当啷声
5. 房客	6. 堕落的；颓废的
7. 习性	
1. atrophy	2. lodger
3. malleable	4. metamorphosis
5. mannerism	

Word List 6

Group 1	
1. 易怒的	2. 极肮脏的；丑恶的
3. 分离主义	4. 活泼的
5. 固执的	6. 摄政王
7. 超过，越过	
1. fractious	2. obstinate
3. overshoot	4. squalid
5. vivacious	

Group 2	
1. 有密切关系的	2. 使人想起…的
3. 陈词滥调	4. 杂种(的)，混血儿(的)
5. 铲平；推倒	6. 举起；掂…的重量
7. 碎石，残余物；废墟	
1. platitude	2. redolent
3. detritus	4. germane
5. heft	

Group 3	
1. 有追溯效力的；追加的	2. 驾驶杆；游戏杆
3. 使在表面形成硬壳	4. 大提琴手
5. 无赖	6. 乳糖
7. 孤芳自赏，自恋	
1. cellist	2. retroactive
3. encrusted	4. rascal
5. narcissism	

Group 4	
1. 快乐	2. 放荡不羁的(人)
3. [生物]果糖	4. 使着迷
5. 阐明	6. 奴役，束缚
7. 熊熊烈火；地狱	
1. bohemian	2. explicate
3. gaiety	4. thrall
5. Ravished	

Group 5	
1. 轻蔑的	2. 征用
3. (使)变形	4. 唐突的
5. 惩罚；磨炼	6. (使成)蜂窝状
7. 无精打采的	
1. languid	2. brusque
3. chastened	4. commandeered
5. pejorative	

Group 6	
1. 诡计	2. 有说服力的
3. (使)交错；(使) 交叉	4. 抨击
5. 倾覆	6. 狂怒的，狂暴的
7. 高谈阔论	
1. ruse	2. berserk
3. cogent	4. diatribe
5. harangue	

Group 7	
1. 下颌(骨)；颚	2. 灌输，教导
3. 泼，溅；搅动，晃动	4. 金丝雀
5. 势利	6. (使)扭曲；歪曲
7. 模范	
1. paragon	2. inculcate
3. contorts	4. snobbery
5. canary	

Group 8	
1. 不热情的	2. 征服
3. 激烈的长篇演说	4. (除去…的)外壳
5. 门房；看门人	6. 诋毁
7. 园艺的	
1. concierge	2. subjugated
3. tepid	4. tirade
5. vilified	

Group 9	
1. 糟透的	2. 等级；阶级
3. 向一侧倾斜的	4. 令人愉快的
5. 破烂的；草率的	6. 锯屑
7. 运动；移动	
1. lopsided	2. gradation
3. abysmal	4. delectable
5. ramshackle	

Group 10	
1. 失礼；失言	2. 凝乳
3. 返祖	4. 苦行的
5. 应受责备的	6. 顽童，小恶魔
7. 对抗，抵消	
1. gaffe	2. imp
3. culpable	4. ascetic
5. countervailing	

Word List 7

Group 1	
1. 专横的	2. 剧毒；致命性
3. 中间休息	4. 灵魔，妖魔
5. 简洁的	6. 顽固的；顽固分子
7. 假内行	
1. laconic	2. intermission
3. peremptory	4. virulence
5. diehard	

Group 2	
1. 日志	2. 专横，跋扈
3. 流浪(者)	4. 下颌；双下巴
5. 天体物理学	6. 变成颗粒状
7. 关切；担心	
1. vagabond	2. domineer
3. granulate	4. solicitude
5. logbook	

Group 3	
1. 小偷小摸	2. 宣泄的
3. 焚毁	4. 刻薄的
5. 使脱水	6. 强调；在字下划横线
7. 纵容	
1. cathartic	2. conniving
3. pilfered	4. incinerated
5. acerbic	

Group 4	
1. 粗鲁的，无礼的	2. 轻松的
3. 最低点	4. 一夫一妻制
5. 阴离子	6. 逗乐的
7. 雕塑	
1. jocular	2. churlish
3. blithe	4. monogamy
5. nadir	

Group 5	
1. 充气	2. 雷电
3. 专制者	4. 同情
5. 漠不关心的	6. (使)凝结
7. 排斥	
1. Aerate	2. ostracized
3. commiserated	4. nonchalant
5. congealed	

Group 6	
1. 吹捧	2. 随意的
3. 尖锐的；犀利的	4. 颤抖的；胆怯的
5. 悔恨，后悔；内疚	6. 愚蠢的
7. 蜂鸟	
1. desultory	2. tremulous
3. compunction	4. trenchant
5. adulation	

Group 7	
1. 内啡肽	2. 莫名其妙的话
3. 使明白易懂	4. 亵渎；破坏
5. 微粒	6. 幽闭恐惧症
7. 拖延	
1. demystify	2. mote
3. desecrated	4. gibberish
5. procrastinate	

Group 8	
1. 险恶的，不诚实的	2. [天文]黑子
3. [皮肤]胼胝；愈合组织；老茧	4. 悲痛的
5. 蹒跚	6. 来回摇摆
7. 盘曲的，蜿蜒的	
1. sinuous	2. snide
3. waggled	4. lugubrious
5. waddle/waddled	

Group 9	
1. 缺乏远见	2. 腰围
3. 硫酸盐	4. 膜的
5. 诡计	6. 使变化
7. 乐意	
1. waistline	2. transmuted
3. subterfuge	4. myopia
5. alacrity	

Group 10	
1. 通知	2. [生物]单体
3. 多情的	4. 大杂烩
5. 可浸入水中的	6. 大火
7. 眩晕	
1. apprise	2. hodgepodge
3. vertigo	4. conflagration
5. amorous	

Word List 8

Group 1	
1. 使混乱	2. 武士精神的；彬彬有礼的
3. 粗暴的	4. 得票多于
5. 变形；美化	6. 解剖学专家
7. 嘲讽	
1. rambunctious	2. gibe
3. chivalrous	4. obfuscate
5. transfiguration	

Group 2	
1. 过分恭维的	2. 刺激的东西
3. 漂浮物	4. 无所不吸收的
5. 抢劫	6. 苍穹
7. 谄媚	
1. fulsome	2. firmament
3. toady	4. omnivorous
5. despoiled	

Group 3	
1. 迟的；缓慢移动的	2. 把…神话；高度赞扬
3. 吸热的	4. 带露水的
5. 头颅	6. 顽固的
7. 催眠的	
1. obdurate	2. cranium
3. soporific	4. tardy
5. deified	

Group 4	
1. 悦耳动听的	2. 未受玷污的
3. [动物学]硬壳	4. 分开
5. 录取	6. 脾气不好的
7. 商人；贩子	
1. mellifluous	2. cantankerous
3. unsullied	4. matriculated
5. fractionated	

Group 5	
1. 逆风	2. 腐烂的
3. 祈祷书	4. 诅骂
5. 有意拖延的	6. 不良气氛或影响
7. 预见	
1. dilatory	2. miasma
3. malediction	4. prescience
5. putrid	

Group 6	
1. 中伤，诽谤	2. 古生物学家
3. 使迷惑；迷惑	4. 拆掉(缝线)，拆开
5. 偷偷摸摸的	6. 刺探隐秘者
7. 坏脾气的	
1. aspersion	2. nonplussed
3. unpicked	4. surreptitious
5. peevish	

Group 7	
1. 减少，减弱	2. 傲慢的
3. 冷淡的	4. 百岁或百岁以上的(人)
5. 有吸附力的	6. 适于销售的
7. (使)堕落，败坏	
1. supercilious	2. debauched
3. bated	4. phlegmatic
5. adsorbent	

Group 8	
1. 抱怨的	2. 变化多端的
3. 刺；刺痛	4. 不成熟的
5. 尖锐的	6. 懒散
7. 堕落者；堕落的	
1. torpor	2. protean
3. querulous	4. callow
5. prickle	

Group 9	
1. 一千年的	2. 厚颜无耻
3. 好战的	4. 恶臭的
5. 五边形	6. 可悲的
7. 鳄鱼(的)	
1. pugnacious	2. malodorous
3. effrontery	4. woefully
5. Crocodilians	

Group 10	
1. 大灾变；大动乱	2. 阴谋集团；共谋
3. [心理学]性虐待	4. 谄媚(者)
5. 逐渐消失的	6. 传统叛逆者
7. 圈套，诈骗，诡计	
1. sycophant	2. evanescent
3. cataclysm	4. chicanery
5. iconoclasts	

Word List 9

Group 1	
1. 妖术的	2. 石板
3. 一片土地或水域	4. 布道坛
5. 自学的人	6. 麻醉剂(的)
7. 严苛的，尖刻的	
1. autodidact	2. scathing
3. tract	4. anesthetic
5. slate	

Group 2	
1. 表示；预示	2. 脱氧核糖核酸
3. 花名册，登记表	4. (涂抹)灰泥，石膏
5. 肥胖，过胖	6. 细枝末节
7. 直觉	
1. betoken	2. corpulence
3. minutiae	4. plaster
5. Gut-level	

Group 3	
1. 使自由，解放	2. 使分裂
3. 光子	4. 担忧，不安
5. 蛋黄	6. 围栏；扶手
7. 枯燥冗长的陈述	
1. litany	2. misgiving
3. railing	4. unfetter
5. splinter	

Group 4	
1. 狂欢，放纵	2. 全面的；重要的
3. 炽热的	4. 长矛
5. 溶解物	6. 倾向
7. 可食的	
1. binge	2. overarching
3. blazing	4. predisposition
5. solute	

Group 5	
1. 冷血动物；变温动物	2. (发出)尖叫声
3. 虚伪言辞	4. 愚蠢的
5. 幼苗	6. 陷阱；引诱…入圈套
7. 栖息	
1. cant	2. dimwitted
3. squealed/squeals	4. snared
5. perching	

Group 6	
1. 更新世	2. 轻击
3. 奸诈的	4. 民俗学者
5. 嗜热动物	6. 码头
7. 鱼群	
1. flicked	2. duplicitous
3. shoal	4. folklorist
5. pier	

Group 7	
1. 灰褐色的；单调的	2. 笨拙的
3. (划)独木舟	4. 吓呆的
5. 装饰花束	6. 覆在上面的
7. 顶峰	
1. petrified	2. drab
3. pinnacle	4. kayak
5. maladroit	

Group 8	
1. 用软布擦亮	2. 海湾
3. 诡计多端的；狡诈的	4. 软骨
5. 随行人员	6. 基因定序
7. 清醒的；冷静的	
1. buff	2. entourage
3. estuary	4. scheme
5. level-headed	

Group 9	
1. 钉牢；确定	2. 大规模抗议
3. 现有的，尚存的	4. 顽强的
5. 碎石	6. 一千年；千禧年
7. (腌制)泡菜	
1. extant	2. dogged
3. rubble	4. mass protest
5. millennium	

Group 10	
1. 葡萄干	2. 轻拍；轻涂
3. 艰巨的，繁重的	4. 使淹没，使覆没
5. 刺耳的	6. 再吸收
7. 整洁的	
1. strenuous	2. whelmed
3. dabbed/dabs	4. spruce
5. cacophony	

Word List 10

Group 1	
1. 致命的，恶毒的	2. 博学的人
3. 急驰	4. 俗丽而不值钱的
5. 批准	6. 郊区牧师
7. 无精打采	
1. slouch	2. careened
3. pernicious	4. savant
5. sanctifies/sanctified	

Group 2	
1. 衣服的底边沿	2. 使习惯于
3. 次要的	4. 夷平，拆毁
5. 大量滋生	6. 杨树
7. 傀儡	
1. inures/inured	2. subservient
3. figurehead	4. raze
5. infested	

Group 3	
1. 诚实	2. 渣滓，糟粕
3. 刺鼻的	4. 撤销，废除
5. 扇贝	6. 柑橘；柑橘树
7. 稻草人	
1. pungent	2. abrogates/abrogated
3. probity	4. scarecrow's
5. Dregs	

Group 4	
1. 表面的，浅薄的	2. 提出，引入
3. 少量，少许(津贴)	4. 激起
5. 射出，排放	6. 麋鹿
7. 鞭打	
1. pittance	2. foment
3. broached/broaches	4. facile
5. whiplashed	

Group 5	
1. 愤怒	2. 蜂窝
3. 窘境，困惑	4. 雪橇
5. 大纲，梗概	6. 手风琴
7. 农学家	
1. quandary	2. pique
3. agronomist	4. beehive
5. synopsis	

Group 6	
1. 激动的	2. 享乐主义
3. 没收；剥夺	4. 睡觉；静止
5. 贪婪的	6. 疑问的
7. 肮脏	
1. slumbered	2. squalor
3. expropriate	4. incandescent
5. Rapacious	

Group 7	
1. [植物]金盏花	2. 可耻的，丢脸的
3. 巨大的	4. 辣味的；开胃的
5. 兀鹫	6. 悔罪的，悔过的(人)
7. 漫步	
1. amble/ambled	2. penitent
3. ignominious	4. piquant
5. gargantuan	

Group 8	
1. 跳水者，潜水者	2. 任性的
3. 富裕的	4. 胰腺
5. 狂风大作的	6. 道貌岸然的
7. 过滤；渗透	
1. percolated	2. cornucopia
3. petulant	4. blusters/blustered
5. pancreatic	

Group 9	
1. (使)过量；(使)充满	2. 雄激素，雄性激素
3. 弄脏	4. 断言
5. 露天剧场	6. 提出异议，驳斥
7. 合同；以契约约束	
1. impugned	2. indentured
3. smudge	4. averred
5. glutted	

Group 10	
1. 偎依	2. 缠住
3. 过度节俭，吝啬	4. (把…送上)断头台
5. 闲荡	6. 强劲的对手
7. 幸运；机会	
1. enmeshed	2. nemesis
3. parsimony	4. snuggles/snuggled
5. moping